MERE MORTALS

Boswell: But of what use will my book be when it is finished?
Johnson: Never mind the use—do it!

History is an Art and should be written with imagination.

ANATOLE FRANCE.

Post Mortems : Two

Mere Mortals

Medico-Historical Essays

By

C. MacLaurin

M.B.C.M., F.R.C.S.E., Hon. Deg. Padua

*Lately Lecturer in Clinical Surgery, the
University of Sydney; Late Consulting
Surgeon, Royal Prince Alfred
Hospital, Sydney; Late Hon-
orary Surgeon, Royal
Hospital for Women,
Sydney*

New  York

George H. Doran Company

MERE MORTALS
— B —
PRINTED IN THE UNITED STATES OF AMERICA

This book is
Affectionately Dedicated
To my Wife
and
To my Daughter
MRS. A. P. MACKERRAS

Preface

GREAT numbers of people, especially medical men, have written to me asking me to continue the short studies of great men of the past that I began in *Post Mortem;* and the result is the present volume.

Many reviewers complained that *Post Mortem* contained too much "medical jargon," whatever that may mean. There is doubtfully such a thing as medical jargon; it is merely a method of expressing thoughts for which there is no English equivalent except by the method of a cumbrous sentence. For that reason I have tried to translate my thoughts into English whenever it is possible. If by mischance a technical term should have crept in, you will find most medical terms in any decent modern English dictionary; or failing that, they are all simply taken from the Greek. But there is another jargon than medical. There is the filthy jargon which insists on saying "the Red Plague" when we mean syphilis; or "in a certain interesting condition" when we mean to say "pregnant."

PREFACE

That jargon I absolutely refuse to use. Those elderly people with fixed minds who prefer that sort of thing had better stick to *Little Arthur* or something equally fictitious. As a doctor writing on very serious subjects I must claim the doctor's privilege of writing with absolute frankness; without suspicion of coarseness.

And I beg you not to accept as diagnoses what are sheer speculations.

Acknowledgments

THE first drafts of these essays appeared in the *Australasian Medical Journal*, *The Sydney Bulletin*, the Australian *Home*, *Art in Australia*, and the Australian *Forum*. They have nearly all been considerably modified with the growth of knowledge and frequent rewriting. I have to thank Miss Kibble, of the New South Wales Public Library, for assisting me immensely in hunting up many authorities from whom I quote. Without her help this book could never have been written.

Glossary

Imperative idea: An idea that, however malapropos it may be, keeps mounting into consciousness.

Obsession: An imperative idea that compels appropriate action.

Phobias: Unconscious fears, often acquired in early infancy, which may ruin a man's whole life for him. There are many different kinds of "phobia" of which syphilophobia is probably the most common.

These three are all signs of:

Psychasthenia: A weird half-sister of neurasthenia, generally the result of heredity, combined with abnormal education in early youth. In the psychasthenic state the patient may be subject to all manner of imperative ideas, obsessions and phobias. Sometimes he stammers, sometimes he is compelled by his "unconscious" to jerk his limbs about in quaint antics; sometimes he is afflicted with awful doubts and scruples.[1]

All the other medical terms are, I think, explained in the text as they arise.

---

[1] There are innumerable English synonyms for psychasthenic, mostly slang. A few are unbalanced, half-crazy, half-cracked, half-dotty, peculiar, queer, etc. But none of these expresses the exact meaning of the Greek; indeed, it is impossible absolutely to escape from medical jargon, except by a phrase.

Contents

Mere Mortals

Dr. Johnson

THERE can be little doubt that the illustrious Dr. Johnson was a psychasthenic. His father could see in life nothing but gloom, though his mother seems to have been hearty and sensible enough. Therefore presumably we are entitled to say that the Great Cham's family history was faulty. At an early age he developed some trouble that his parents diagnosed as scrofula, or tuberculous glands of the neck, but Boswell expressly hints was suspected to have been caught from a nurse. They took him to England's kindly but not intelligent majesty, Queen Anne, who, wearing a long black hood and diamonds to impress her patients, touched him for his "grievous malady." But she did not cure him; rather it would seem that she made him worse; for all Johnson's frightful jerkings and grimaces, roarings and puffings, may possibly be traced back to that one moment of nervous tension when he felt himself a little boy, the observed of all observers, waiting to be touched by the sister-in-law of William the Dutchman.

17

A child of bad heredity—indeed any child— must be treated with the utmost care long before it appears to be conscious, before it appears to take notice of what is going on around it; quarrelsome parents and angry nurses may so warp his whole mental outlook that it is spoiled for life. And it could not have been a good thing for the coming Great Cham to subject him to such nervous strain as was necessarily involved in taking him before Queen Anne. He was lucky in that it did not make him stammer. Many a sensitive boy has been made to stammer by less than was involved in Sam's childish treatment. Long before a child appears to be conscious its mind is taking notice of all that goes on around it, and its whole future life may be warped in one moment of terror or anxiety. And the sad thing is that probably Mrs. Johnson senior had made a mistake in diagnosis, that probably little Sam was not suffering from scrofula at all, but from some swelling of the glands of the neck that was due to something in his scalp. That he lived till he was seventy-five seems to show that he never suffered either from tuberculosis or syphilis, those two great slayers; and if his glands had really been tuberculous it is probable that, bursting, they would have formed a "mixed infection" that would have had more serious effects than mere local scarring.

It is possible that while the incident persisted in Johnson's conscious memory as a "confused and solemn memory," in his unconscious memory it may have persisted in those extraordinary antics which to Boswell seemed a sort of St. Vitus's dance. Perhaps in them we see the struggles of a sensitive little boy to avoid the frightful ordeal of being "touched" and resentment at the insult to his masculine grandeur. We know that his masculinity had already been very much insulted at the age of three when a schoolmistress ran after him lest he fall into the gutter.

Psychasthenia is a grim half-sister to neurasthenia, from which it appears to differ in that, while neurasthenia merely shows that the man's nervous system is not sufficiently strong to stand the stout clouts and buffets of this wicked world, in psychasthenia he has never had a chance. The best translation of the term "psychasthenic" appears to be "unbalanced," and, though probably psychasthenia was about the best term that Professor Janet could have selected for this queer condition, still it conveys an unwarranted implication of imbecility, for many men of the greatest genius have been utterly unbalanced. The man of genius is seldom actually insane, but he is often unbalanced and of the manic-depressive temperament; at any moment he may be "knocked off his perch" and may become definitely insane.

Thus, subject always to the possible denial of the alienists, I should certainly imagine that Beethoven was psychasthenic, for he was always falling in and out of love, was constantly quarrelling with his landlords, cast his rice pudding at the cook, jammed his hat fiercely on his head when he and Goethe walked before royalty, was looked upon as crazy, and used to run about the fields trying to roar the latest melody that had come into his head. And Charles Lamb not only stammered but had a sister who was definitely insane.

The unbalanced are subject to queer actions which appear to take their origin in the unconscious mind. Thus, there arise from the unconscious into consciousness imperative ideas which insist on recognition however malapropos they may happen to be. Sometimes these actually go on to form obsessions, and I must ask you to permit me to define these two important terms. The imperative idea simply arises into consciousness out of the unconscious. When it compels appropriate action it is generally, though not always, called an obsession. Thus, when Johnson walked along Fleet Street the imperative idea arose from his unconscious that it would be a fitting thing to put his hand upon every horse-post that he passed. When he did so or turned on his tracks that no horse-post should be left uncapped the definition of an obsession would appear to be correct. And from the unconscious arise those queer phobias or fears which often so strangely influence their actions.

Still gossiping about the unbalanced, was St. Francis of Assisi entirely sane when he left all the money that he owed his father on a heap of his clothes and set out to build a church with his own hands? If this be insanity let us have more of it. The ordinary sane stodgy man does not lead the world; secure in his stodginess he makes money and lives happy ever after. But the genius is always a little "cracked," otherwise he would probably not be a genius. And so many of them have been ill men; in fact one can hardly call to mind as one writes a single really healthy and sane genius, unless possibly Sir Walter Scott. St. Francis is said to have had renal tuberculosis.

That is probably the only real serious objection to birth-control; you can never tell whom you are condemning to perpetual absence of life. Thus

Abraham Lincoln, strictly speaking, should never have been born, for his mother, Nancy Hanks, though never insane, lived all her life in the depths of gloom and on the verge of insanity. Yet it would appear that the absence of Old Abe at a given crisis of the world's history might have made some difference to civilisation. And even if we are to take bodily health as the criterion of fitness, what about Mozart, the tuberculous and pallid little genius of Vienna whom many people still consider as the very greatest musician that ever lived? Certainly not even Beethoven in his first period ever attained to Mozart's delicious childlikeness of touch.

If the world had insisted that St. Francis of Assisi, Abe Lincoln, and Wolfgang Amadeus Mozart should not have been born one would think that the world would now be a poorer place than it is. And one names only a few; for Spinoza should never have been born, doomed to live only a few years and then to die of tuberculosis while he was mystically trying to reduce God to a mathematical formula.

In fact one could go on for weeks on this subject, and the conclusion that any fair-minded person must reach is that birth-control, even of the apparently unfit, is too risky an experiment for the human race to try if it wishes to keep its geniuses. You never can tell what the infant may turn out that you are preventing from being born. But I am aware that this is a highly contentious subject, and that awful thing, "the sex-war," is involved in it. People are sure to have differences of opinion about it; since woman has risen to her new estate these opinions will assuredly be held with more vigour than ever.

"Treat 'em rough" is a known and tried aphorism, which has been elevated to a pitch of almost epic grandeur by Schopenhauer's "Pitch 'em downstairs"; and probably some such aphorism was in Johnson's mind when he rode with old Mrs. Porter to the church that they might be married, and, you remember, reduced her to tears before they got there. Up till then he probably had only the poet's knowledge of woman; but that after such an ill beginning the marriage turned out so happily, seems to argue that Mrs. Porter, though she might paint her face, was nevertheless a woman with the heart of a lion to tame his aggressively masculine soul. And it is quite possible that before she died—she was twice his age, you know—he began to have for her a love similar to that one has for a mother. Of course it may be that Boswell, in his uncomplimentary description of Johnson's wife, was misled by jealousy of her who sat too near the throne of his hero-worship. But in any case she must have been a remarkable woman to tame Ursa Major as she did.

If one were to translate psychasthenic into "poor in spirit"—which is not very far from its Greek meaning—probably we should come very near to its real inner meaning; and we have the best possible authority for knowing the post-mortem future of the poor in spirit. If the Kingdom of Heaven is to be composed of such men as Johnson and Beethoven it would not be a bad place to inhabit, though the shade of Johnson would certainly insist on carrying home some fallen angel, while Beethoven would probably throw something at a monotonous orchestra of harps, if he could hear it.

In support of the contention that towards the end of her life he had begun to consider Mrs. Porter as less a wife in the ordinary sense of the term than a mother-surrogate whom he could trust as a faithful friend who would never desert him whatever the circumstances, here is a letter that he wrote to the Rev. Dr. Taylor on the day she died:

"Sir,

"Pray desire Mrs. Taylor to inform me what
mourning I should buy for my mother and Miss
Porter, and bring a note of writing with you."

His dear wife dead he could not trust himself
even to buy mourning without her aid.

He appears not to have been able even to take
care of himself without some woman to act the
mother towards him. Years later he found another mother-surrogate in Mrs. Thrale, who saw
to it that he wore respectable clothing with brass
buttons, and silver buckles—not too big—on his
shoes. It was evidently a severe blow to him
when the naughty thing went and married Signor
Piozzi, for it left him without a single woman to
show him how to take care of himself.

That nervous malady which Boswell diagnosed
as a sort of St. Vitus's dance probably merely
represented the violent impulsive and involuntary
movements occasionally seen in psychasthenia;
had the defect affected the nerves of speech Johnson would probably have stammered; but one can
never imagine a man so aggressive stammering.

How far back in life is it possible to remember? Freud thinks that the first five years of life
are not retained in conscious memory, although

they exercise the greatest possible influence upon our afterlives. Personally I try to think that my first recollection is that of the frightful itching that accompanied the wearing of my first pair of knickerbockers, which my mother used to tell me occurred on my fourth birthday; but it is so difficult to distinguish between what you remember and what older people have told you that one must sometimes think that after all probably Freud may be right, and it is impossible to remember before the fifth birthday.

Johnson's roars and bluster were probably really to conceal an innate shyness that is frequently seen in very nervous men. In further evidence that he was at heart a shy man here is a letter that he wrote to his old friend Dr. Birch:

" March 29, 1765.

"To Dr. Birch,

"Sir:

"I have sent some parts of my dictionary, such as were at hand, for your inspection. The favour which I ask of you is that if you do not like them, you will say nothing.

"I am, sir,

"Your most affectionate humble servant,

"SAM JOHNSON."

He could not even bear to hear the faithful words of his old friend about the child of his brain, though he felt himself entitled to sign "your most affectionate humble servant."

Like most men of apparently strong common sense, when you look too critically into their dogmata, Johnson's common sense begins to look more like uncommon foolishness; for it was certainly no answer to Bishop Berkeley's metaphysics to bang his foot against a stone. It requires a far more subtle argument which must probably be fortified by the eye of faith, which, you remember, has been defined as "the faculty of believing what you know to be untrue." But Johnson's argument is the sort of bluff obvious thing that so appeals to a common-sense person like John Bull. And doubtless that is why Johnson has so appealed to John Bull that he has almost been elevated to the pinnacle of a national hero. Full of rats, poor old gentleman; yet one can't help loving him for his rats.

As woman seldom stammers, so she is seldom afflicted by psychasthenia, which, being a variation, appears to be almost confined to the male, like genius. Woman is seldom "ratty"; she has far too much hard common sense. Who ever heard of women killing each other to settle whether a word should be spelt homooisian or homoousian? Or to decide whether there are three Gods or One? Yet men have waged savage tumult over these very things, which no person can possibly know. Sometimes lady novelists seem to go ratty when they try to describe men, and ultimately describe some creature who is like nothing on earth; but it is only fair to say that such lady novelists are suspected by men to be between the ages of forty and fifty, and probably for a time slightly unbalanced. But the normal average woman is far saner than the normal average man. Once she has secured her man her chief duty afterwards seems to be to see that his rats do not lead him away from the paths of respectability, into such nonsense as that of Bernard Palissy, for instance, who burned even his furniture to keep the stove going that might lead to the discovery of a porcelain glaze, even though his wife and children might starve. No woman ever followed a will-o'-the-wisp with such fury, simply because no woman was ever so ratty; it is hardly respectable; it seems to be purely a matter of sex-physiology.

But we must dilate yet a little further on the utterly unbalanced character of Johnson. An incident is told of him in 1784, when he was about 74 years of age; as it is impossible to tell it better than Boswell, let us leave it in Boswell's own words. "Coming home late one night he found a poor woman lying in the street, so much exhausted that she could not walk; he took her upon his back" (by the way it was a quite unnecessarily laborious and cumbersome way to carry a woman; for a giant like Sam it would have seemed an easier matter to stoop down and pick her up in his arms), "and carried her to his home, where he found her to be one of those wretched females who have sunk to the lowest levels of vice, poverty, and disease. Instead of upbraiding her he had her taken care of with all care and tenderness for a long time at considerable expense, till she was restored to health and endeavoured to put her into a virtuous way of living." This was just the sort of kind, impulsive, and senseless thing that would seem so utterly natural to a psychasthenic and so utterly silly to a normal man. We know now that it is almost impossible to reclaim a prostitute, for no normal woman ever becomes a prostitute. Normal woman always has far too much dignity and self-respect and reads too mystic a meaning into the sexual act ever to offer herself to the embraces of any casual man in the street, however great her economic distress; rather if driven into a corner by poverty a normal woman finds some one male friend to help her, so that she may console herself with the thought that at least she is married in the sight of God, if not in the sight of man. Normal woman is essentially monogamous. But Sam appears to have been as hopeful of success as Theodora when she made her famous raid upon the brothels of Byzantium; one would like to know the ultimate success or failure of his adventure into the underworld. We know that poor Theodora failed absolutely. One cannot help wondering what Anna Williams would have thought of it, for women are the enemies of women; but fortunately for her she seems to have been recently dead, having quarrelled with everyone who was open to quarrel with her. If this be true, at least she never knew to what depths of degradation Samuel could sink. But a doctor can easily imagine the fulsome gratitude that would be lavished by the poor starving prostitute upon the huge preserver when she woke up and found him giving her something to eat without wanting anything else from her. Prostitutes do not meet with so much disinterested kindness in this world that it ever palls. That is why it is so sad that sexual reclamation of them is almost impossible, for too often they carry the seeds of their own destruction with them.

Then there is that delicious incident of Mr. Osborn the bookseller. "The fellow insulted me, so I beat him; but it was in the privacy of my own chamber—it was not in his shop." Of course. To knock down a publisher was only quite right and proper. Who would not do it? But even a publisher has his rights. To do it in his own shop would be to expose him to the insults of his own servants, and that is positively not done, especially by an Oxford man. Rats, pure rats. Yet publishers are said to be fair game for authors and so far no close-season has been proclaimed for them.

Few men attain to the age of seventy odd without some warning that they are mortal and that the grave is waiting. Of course there is the classic instance of Voltaire, who from the age of sixty odd complained of mortal illness, and yet, recovering, lived to a vast age, wizened, malicious, and "peaky" as a rat. But then, like Mr. Blake, Voltaire was a regular out and out hardened sinner and words could not possibly express the contempt that he felt for the mediæval devil of eighteenth-century Christianity. Probably he persisted in living on just to cheat the devil of his just due because he despised him so.

As a matter of fact we often find that soon

after fifty some illness attacks a man from which he never really recovers, even though he may appear to be well; there is always the trifling difference in him that marks the passage of the years. Johnson's warning came to him—though he did not observe it—many years before when Boswell could observe the sight that he made of himself as he gobbled his meals.

He was evidently very fond of eating; himself, he boasted of his delicate tastes in food; and when he ate "the veins of his forehead stood out and a strong perspiration was visible." This appears to have much disgusted Macaulay, but most of us have seen similar prowess in perfectly worthy men. Presumably when Boswell said "the veins of his forehead" he meant the superficial temporal arteries, for if they had really been the soft and thin-walled veins, Johnson, bestrewn with bladders, would have looked indeed noteworthy. But there came a time when they stood out once too often, and probably they never shrank back again to the normal size, but became thickened. Thus his blood-pressure rose under the strain of arteriosclerosis and in the course of years the inevitable results of gluttony overtook him. Drink, guzzle, and syphilis are the three deadly sins, and they are deadly in proportion to the effect that they cause upon the arteries. And in the term "arteries" one includes heart and kidneys. The heart is simply a large expansion of an artery, and the kidneys are merely a network of arterioles and capillaries; if one part goes all the rest follow, and thus it is that the term "cardiovascular disease" is generally used to describe the results of high blood-pressure. It is of course possible that Johnson's glooms may have been due to intestinal auto-intoxication; but melancholia is a constant companion of an unduly sensitive nervous system.

Warnings came in 1782 with breathlessness and pain in the chest; the heart was evidently beginning to rebel, but the first real alarming warning came on the night of June 17th, 1783, when he awoke in the middle of the night and found that he could not speak. Trying to write, he found that "my hand made wrong letters," that is to say he had not only aphasia, but "agraphia" or loss of power to write. Possibly if anybody had happened to think of it he might have been able to communicate with the outer world by means of children's block letters. But nobody did; and when his servant came in the morning he could not comprehend why the old gentleman expected him to read something that he had written instead of speaking in answer to his own chatter.

This sudden aphasia in old people is not uncommon, and may be due to several causes, that all in one way or other affect the so-called "speech centre" of the brain. As the "writing centre" is situated in the very near vicinity, it is not surprising that a lesion that affects one generally also affects the other. That Johnson's right hand was not also paralysed at the same time is rather unusual, because the left side of the brain which controls the right side of the body also contains the speech centre; and it is supposed that it does so because man has for many thousands of years been accustomed to use his right hand more than his left, wherefore the left side of his brain would naturally be more ready to acquire new functions than the right, which only controls the comparatively awkward left hand. If this theory be true it would rather seem to show that men were accustomed to use their right hands long before they could speak; and this indeed is quite probable.

The exact lesion would appear to have been that one of the cerebral arteries that supplied the left side of Johnson's brain had for some reason been thrown into a state of spasm, and caused temporary softening of the brain owing to interference with its blood-supply. If an artery had actually burst on the site of a tiny aneurysm, as occasionally happens in cases of arteriosclerosis, the old man would not have recovered so soon, even temporarily. As it was, he seems to have recovered sufficiently by July to pay a visit to Dr. Langton at Rochester. The shock and terror induced by an attack of aphasia are generally very dreadful. I remember one elderly lady, who had always been of a most gentle and virtuous way of living, who one day suddenly sat up in bed with a scream, clutching at her bedclothes and at her throat and uttering meaningless noises like an ape. Twelve hours later she had for a time recovered her power of speech, and after lying musing for half an hour, said in her customary gentle voice, "I should like some fish; they say fish is good for the brain." She had somewhere read that fish contains a large amount of phosphorus, which is supposed to be good for the brain—by patent-medicine vendors. But I shall never forget the scream of that poor lady, nor the look of terror that came over her gentle face.

Johnson's terror led him to write a prayer for his recovery, done in Latin verse. "The lines were not very good, but I knew them to be not very good, so concluded that I was not impaired in my faculties." There you see at once the supreme passion of the man—Learning—coming out in what he thought to be the very article of death.

Then, "in order to rouse the vocal organs, I took two drams. Wine has been celebrated for the production of eloquence, so I put myself into violent motion and I think repeated it; but all was in vain." It is hardly fair to comment upon this action of a man bemused with terror and aphasia that probably wine was the very worst thing he could have taken; for it tends to raise the blood-pressure. Not that it made much difference; Death was focussing his eyes on Dr. Johnson; the call was coming, and no earthly power could avert it.

But apparently even Boswell nods; for after telling of Johnson's terrible illness in 1783 he goes on to tell how in *1784* he was able to put a woman on his back and carry her home. Well, one simply does not believe it; the thing is impossible; Boswell must have got his dates mixed a little; for to carry a woman, even though she were starving and the man a giant, is no small feat; and if the man were very old and had just recovered from an attack of aphasia, it would be absolutely incredible. Really, wonderful though we men are—in no way more wonderful than in our power of believing nonsense—we are not such terrible fellows as some say.

After the paralytic stroke all the devils in hell seem to have settled upon the poor old gentleman, with their gout, dropsy, and continual fear of death. Probably the gout was simply another manifestation of the defect of metabolism—faulty chemical physiological process, or dystrophy—that had caused his high blood-pressure. The asthma and oppression in his chest were probably due to a failing heart; and thence also doubtless came the dropsy; for dropsy is not a disease—it is a symptom of many things, generally cardiac or renal. And his cough became exceedingly troublesome, possibly due to congestion of the base of his lungs that would be caused in a way much the same as caused the dropsy; he was becoming "water-logged."

A rather remarkable thing is that, once having become filled up with dropsy, he got rid of it apparently suddenly. If I remember rightly Dr. Johnson was taking squills at the time, and squills is still used for getting rid of fluid from the body, though it has been supplanted by more efficient drugs. One might perhaps think that hope told Johnson a flattering tale, but he says expressly that he got rid of twenty pints. Queer things happen in dropsy, and even such a pseudo-miracle as Johnson's is not unknown. Once water-logged with dropsy, legs, belly, lungs and all, it would have seemed to require a miracle to get him emptied, and miracles seldom happen.

The really wonderful thing is, however, that a man of so gloomy a temperament as the Great Cham should have retained such comparative cheerfulness of spirits as he had even after an experience so depressing as an attack of aphasia. He must have been a remarkably brave old man, which is quite in accordance with his strongly masculine character. And this discovery of the wrong dating of one of the most remarkable things that Boswell tells of him only makes his conduct more heroic; for if what I surmise is true, Miss Williams must have been alive and quarrelsome, ready to give Sam the rough side of her tongue for daring to carry home a woman of abandoned character. Cynics have said that to marry a woman is to marry a conscience; but it is even more terrible when the woman is not a man's wife, but, old, blind, deaf, and quarrelsome, is dependent on his generosity for a living. She may probably consider it her duty to look after his morals as strictly as though she were his wife.

His actual end seems to have been caused by a mild terminal pneumonia, which in a healthy young person would have been thrown off like a cold in the head; but was too much for ancient lungs and tired heart.

"To be miserable," said Goldsmith, who had known what it was to be inarticulate and despised, "was to ensure the protection of Dr. Johnson." Was not that a better definition of sainthood than whimsically to pervert the Sermon on the Mount?

To sum up, probably all Johnson's psychasthenic involuntary movements, which made him so strange a figure to his contemporaries, took their origin in unconscious memory of some affront to his childish masculinity, such as would be caused by taking him to Queen Anne to be "touched." And she was not even a king, nor yet even in the direct line of accession either! These women! They will go poking their noses in everywhere.

And possibly here too many have been the source of those extraordinary imperative ideas which it was dangerous to deny, lest he roar at you for an ignorant and intolerant fellow. Assuredly you cannot treat a child too carefully if you want it to grow up a sane and normal member of the human race.

King Henry the Saint

IT was probably because of his unfair treatment when he was a child that Henry VI of pathetic memory was driven "psychasthenic" in its etymological meaning of "weak-souled." His father was Henry V, the strong man of Agincourt; his mother Katherine of Valois, herself the daughter of a lunatic. This little boy, of unsound heredity, was born at Windsor while his father was fighting in France, and barely was he five months old when his mother bethought her that her duty was by the side of her husband. She therefore left her baby to the care of a wet-nurse while she herself crossed the Channel. At that time Henry V was sickening for the illness which was soon to kill him. Probably it was the result of hard fighting and worry, together with, as was so often the case with fifteenth-century kings, eating too much.

When he was less than two years old his faithful lieges of the House of Commons asked that they might see him; so mother, nurse and baby set off in "chairs" from Windsor to London. On a certain Saturday they reached Staines, on the banks of the Thames, and on the following day they had purposed to journey to London. But alas! this defilement of the Sabbath so horrified the little king, then doubtless "teething," that he set up a vast hullabaloo: so bitterly did he weep that the distracted mother and nurse had perforce to take him back to his lodgings, where doubtless the maternal slipper bore its part in his education, for the horrified chronicler tells us that she used every effort. This may have been the first of the famous thrashings that little Henry received, though probably there had been others; in fact, his boyhood seems, to put it crudely, to have been one long wallop. The day of rest having been passed in consoling the infant, and no doubt giving him teething powders or dill-water, and other days having arrived by effluxion of time, they finally got him up to Westminster, where doubtless he twiddled his toes and "gooed" before an admiring concourse of members of Parliament. Soon afterwards the privy council appointed another nurse, probably because the first had so signally failed to smother his bawlings when his subjects had wished to see him. To her he gave an edict that she was to use "every effort to reasonably chastise Us on meet occasion"; so it was clear that chastisement bulked largely in the thoughts of fifteenth-century educationists in dealing with Henry VI.

When he was five he opened Parliament in person, and was set upon a horse to ride throughout London, where the lieges remarked upon the wonderful likeness he bore to the "lovely countenance" of his illustrious father. Quite probably there was a certain amount of imagination in this remark, because everybody knows how a lump of putty on a baby's face is stoutly asserted by an adoring nurse to be the living image of the noble Roman nose of its father. The imagination of nurses is indeed wonderful.

Then he was, by the terms of his father's will, put into the hands of the Earl of Warwick as preceptor. Warwick is generally held to have been the model of a preceptor, but one has doubts; for in after years, when Henry had reached the years of articulate complaint, he meekly spoke to the privy council of the thrashings that he had had to endure. Byron has well summed up the orthodox method of instruction:

"O ye who teach the ingenuous youth of nations,
England, France, Holland, Italy or Spain;
I pray you chastise them on all occasions;
It mends their morals—never mind the pain."

42

And as the House of Lancaster was nothing if not orthodox I have no doubt that the good Earl did his duty faithfully by his pupil.

Next he had to be crowned King of England; and the ceremony seems to have been distinguished by the inordinate number of times that the archbishop had to strip the little boy to his undershirt and make him don other robes. A collection of clerics had to assist him off the platform staggering under the weight of that crown which was to prove too heavy for him when the murderous political uproar of the Wars of the Roses came to pass.

Then they took him to Paris to crown him King of France, by order of his father, who, dying, still considered himself the great conqueror of France. According to Miss Christie, biographer of Henry VI, the English did everything possible on the occasion to hurt the feelings of the French, but probably little Henry quite enjoyed the service, just like a modern schoolboy. At any rate he got away for a time from his preceptor, who had been busily employed as gaoler to Joan of Arc, treating her with quite unnecessary savagery.

Then came the long process of making peace with France after the Hundred Years' War. It seems to have consisted of each side making truces which were meant to be broken as soon as made. Then, when he was twenty-three, his subjects ordered their meek king to get him a wife, and after a hunt with varying fortunes among all the princesses of Western Europe who seemed likely to suit, he selected Margaret of Anjou, an exceedingly pretty and lively girl with whose portrait he fell in love. She was then sixteen, and set off for England with high hopes on both sides. Alas! once more the pathetic tragi-comedy of poor Henry VI's life displayed itself; for the crossing was terribly rough, and Margaret was desperately sea-sick. Henry rushed to meet her, doubtless to see if she was as pretty as her picture, but she had caught chicken-pox on the ship and he had to postpone the wedding until the pretty bride recovered. Her experience was almost like that of some English brides, who, reaching Melbourne, have found the mosquitoes so attentive that they have come on to Sydney a mere simulacrum of the blooming fresh beauty that had got on board the ship so hopefully at Tilbury Docks.

Six years later, when the Wars of the Roses were coming into full blast and England was rent in twain by quarrels among aristocratic families which were only to be settled by the rise of the heavy-handed Tudors, she bore him his only son;

but the effort was disastrous not to her, but to poor young Henry himself. The anxiety, both over her and over his distracted country, had driven him "melancholy," and he developed well-marked melancholia.[1] While the king lay helpless and silly, unable even to take cognisance of his new-born son when Margaret held it up to him, Margaret took the leadership of England into her own strong hands.

One cannot help wondering how Margaret got on with the nursing. As she was just about to become a mother herself she could not have been very strong; certainly not strong enough to nurse a great big helpless baby as well as her own tiny pink little new-born. Probably she got the duchess of this or the countess of that to do the bulk of the work—for nursing is hard work. There is far more in it than merely fanning a fevered brow and talking romantic nonsense to a helpless man. One often sees two little energetic women go to a bedside, grasp a sick man where it will not hurt him, and then in the twinkling of an eye, he, a mass of incarnate pain, has been moved to an entirely new position with never a twinge. But— they are *professional* nurses; it has taken them

[1] Probably it was the clinical type with stupor, in which grief and the sense of sin become so overwhelming that the patient can hardly move.

45

years to learn the little trick. It does not come to woman by a special gift of God. The most fervent wifely devotion does not compensate for its absence. We saw a great deal of these aristocratic amateur nurses during the war; there was a certain royal lady who sometimes used to help me at operations in London, and a great big kindhearted smiling woman she was, though not very intelligent. But if she made a blunder—and it was never very serious—she always passed it off with so happy a smile that we always overlooked it.

If my reading of Queen Margaret's character is correct she was a very determined though not very wise young woman, and if her assistant made a bad break doubtless she felt the rough edge of the queen's tongue. But the main thing was that poor silly young Henry recovered and his wife was able to get on with her war without being worried by anything worse than the normal troubles of a nursing mother.

If she had been a woman before, nursing her saintly husband as if he had been her son, she became a tigress now that she had a real son of her own to fight for; and we have a vivid picture of her raising an army for the House of Lancaster:

"Many assembled for love they bare to the king, but more for the fear they had for the queen, whose countenance was so terrible and whose look was so fearful that to all men against whom she took a small displeasure her frouning was their undoing and her indignation was their death."

Could this furious mænad have been the same as the pretty girl who landed, eager, seasick, and ready for chicken-pox, just before her wedding?

We need not go through the whole melancholy history of the Wars of the Roses, which were really just the fifteenth-century murderous way of holding a general election, but without even our modern profession of principles. Everybody knows how Edward IV became king in one of the temporary lulls, how Henry VI, after another attack of melancholia, was captured in spite of the efforts of his strenuous wife; and how, at the battle of Bosworth Henry VII killed his rival Richard of Gloucester, and at last began modern history with the iron rule of the Tudors. Many of us have been to St. Albans, and will be interested in the two particularly savage elections that were held in that city; by a strange misnomer they have been called battles. The wounded used to run into the vast old cathedral for shelter while

47

the election raged furiously up and down the pleasant streets of that dear old town. Of all the houses that looked down upon the fighting and resounded to the roar of the newly invented cannon I suppose that the only ones still standing are the cathedral itself and the ancient hostelry at which so many of us have had afternoon tea.

Edward IV imprisoned poor hapless Henry for years; but at last the redoubtable Warwick the Kingmaker restored the rightful—and by that time melancholic and imbecile—monarch to the throne, amid general rejoicings. His second reign lasted only ten months, terminating in the Tower. There can be little doubt that Richard of Gloucester murdered him privily therein. In 1910 his remains were dug up, and his thin light skull was found with its remnants of hair still plastered with blood.

It would appear that King Henry took to religion as a means of escape from the miseries of his youth. Probably he felt that in the Church only could he see the slightest sign of sympathy for little overthrashed boys.

He was the gentlest and most virtuous of men. The most violent oath that even his worst sufferings ever wrung from his lips was "Forsoothe and forsoothe," sometimes varied by "Fie for shame."

Queen Margaret could have done better. Once he fled from a ball because the clothes of the ladies displayed more than he thought proper. But even the fury of Margaret could not protect him when Richard Hunchback found him in the way.

Henry's obsessions took the form of impulsive and senseless generosity to his supposed friends, and of singing unduly loudly in church. Though he was meek enough, Richard of Gloucester showed him that he could not inherit the earth, and according to some religions Margaret, being a woman, would never have been allowed to show him the way past the golden gate into the kingdom of heaven.

Poor, gentle, virtuous Henry; so well-meaning, yet so overwhelmed by the sense of his sin!

And poor tigerish Margaret of Anjou! If she had had sense enough to "come in out of the wet" we might now be saying "Good Queen Peggy" instead of "Good Queen Bess." But how can you expect a woman to show common sense and self-restraint when she knows they are attacking her only son? They killed him at last at Tewkesbury almost before her eyes, and thenceforward Margaret became a very tigress and was always intriguing with Louis XI to avenge herself upon the Yorkists.

King Henry VIII

"Never ask me," said John Hunter, "what I have said or written, but ask me what my present opinions are and I will tell you."

"Know syphilis in all its manifestations and relations, and all other things clinical shall be added unto you."—OSLER.

IT is extraordinary what a popular aversion there seems to be to the idea that this man had syphilis, and that many of his actions were due to his syphilis. To judge by the number of letters that I have received from both England and America one would be inclined to think that he was suffering from measles. This I interpret in two ways: firstly, that people still cling to the idea that syphilis is a "loathsome disease"; secondly, that they do not wish to have their pet ideal of a monster rationally explained in medical terms. As a matter of fact, syphilis is far more than a loathsome disease of skin and bone; it would be quite as reasonable to call it often a very grim disease of brain, mind, soul and body. Since the general use of mercury its skin and bone manifestations have sunk into comparative harmlessness, and since the general use of the arsenobenzol compounds the disease seems to have become still less dangerous to the body; but there is always before us the fact that it may be a very terrible affliction for mind and nervous tissues. But people love to hug their little delusions, and so long as they cling to the idea that it is only a "loathsome disease," so long will syphilis continue to destroy the flower of the human race— hard-working intellectual middle-aged men who once upon a time were very human youths.

And there seems to be a misconception about its hereditary nature. The child of a syphilitic may be apparently healthy in appearance, though its resistance to other diseases may be low; it would need a blood examination by Wassermann's test to make sure that its troubles were really syphilitic. It need not necessarily show the classical symptoms of "snuffles," wasting, and rash. All that may happen is that its whole body resisting power is damaged, and it falls a prey to one or other of the innumerable disease germs that are always ready to attack us.

Furthermore, so virulent is sectarian prejudice

that almost every single point about Henry's life seems still to be in dispute. If anybody could tell me a safe track through the maze of conflicting accounts of the reign of Henry Tudor, between the modern feminists who still cling to the idea that he was an unspeakable monster, the Roman Catholic Church which still paints him as the very devil, Froude who hailed him as the great Protestant hero of the Reformation, and the accounts of the ordinary man who looks upon him as a blood-thirsty spot of grease—I believe Charles Dickens used that elegant description—I should welcome it; but as I have no criterion of truth but what medical experience has shown me to be true of men, women and disease, I can only follow the account of him given by Professor Pollard, who, treating him with studied moderation, was prepared to consider him as the "great Erastrian," the protagonist of State against Church. No doubt that is substantially true. It is not for a doctor to say.

Even the number of premature births endured by his wives is in dispute; and all sorts of cock-and-bull stories are made up to show that his children, if born alive, or his wives if they took ill were singularly subject to the effects of cold and overlong christenings. Once would be all very well; but when it happens more than once it becomes suspicious. It is wonderful what people can invent when they wish to explain a thing by religious and political conspiracies—of which they can really *know* nothing in an age so utterly different from ours, in which the actors have long gone beyond our intimate knowledge—when the obvious medical truth is staring them in the face. Human beliefs have changed, but syphilis is still the same.

I follow Pollard because he impresses me as a man of common sense. I have not met him; but the sheer virulent abuse of the ordinary man is no argument and is a better description of the critic's own mind than of his subject.

The facts which can only reasonably be explained by the idea that he was suffering from constitutional syphilis are as follows—I put them in the order in which they impress myself:

(*a*) The extraordinary number of premature births and dead children from two of his wives, one of whom was young and healthy. The early death of Catherine's first-born son is attributed to the strain of a long christening on a bitter midwinter day.

(*b*) The poor health of at least three of his children, Mary Tudor, Edward VI, and the illegitimate Duke of Richmond; whether Elizabeth escaped the infection is at least doubtful since Professor Chamberlain has carefully investigated the details of her health.

(*c*) The terrible degeneration, mental, moral, and physical, which set in in his early middle age.

(*d*) The facts contained in the extract from the *British Medical Journal* of 1910: "From being an able and athletic man he had become a mass of loathsome infirmities. He was bloated in face and so unwieldy that he could hardly pass through an ordinary door. His legs were swollen and covered with festering sores, causing an unbearable stench. Towards the end those about him saw that death was at hand, though, according to Foxe, he would never allow it to be mentioned in his hearing. Kings never seem to have liked it to be recognised that they are mortal, in which reluctance to face facts they are much like other people."

(*e*) The sinus in his leg which caused him unbearable agony whenever it was closed. This seems to have been syphilitic periostitis occurring in an essentially neurotic man.

(*f*) Death in stupor at the comparatively early age of fifty-five.

Not any single one of these symptoms is indubitable evidence of syphilis, but taken altogether there is no other reasonable explanation. In syphilis and self-indulgence we have the secret of the whole tragic development of this king's character. Syphilis alone would doubtfully have accounted for it, even less perhaps gluttonous and bibulous self-indulgence. It is quite true that after his first marriage he seems to have abandoned all moral restraint, or at least guidance by ecclesiastics and the Church; but his dreadful degeneration was not a result of doing so; he did so because he was influenced by the spirochæte and gluttony combined. To-day, when a man gets into gaol for any particularly shameless offence—especially sexual—the very first thing that the police surgeon does is to perform a Wassermann test upon his cerebro-spinal fluid; and I am perfectly certain that if it were possible to do so upon Henry Tudor, the report would come back marked "Wassermann plus," and probably towards the end of his life "plus plus plus!"

But when did he catch it? He does not seem to have *obviously* infected any of his wives, so far as we can tell, so the inference is that he must have caught it several years before he married Catherine of Aragon. Well, he married her when he was little more than eighteen, so he must have caught it when he was thirteen or fourteen, at about the very earliest that a gay and showy boy of the Renaissance could manage to catch it. Then probably the primary lesion, so apparently innocent and harmless, healed up under the influence of some simple ointment,[2] just as it does to-day in thousands of men, who bitterly rue later the one little slip that was to cause them all their woes—and Henry went his life through, probably having quite forgotten the trifling incident. To this day we find that those cases of syphilis which are trifling at first, are just the very cases which, under the influence of worry, lack of treatment, or overstrain, go so tragically wrong at the end. The somewhat wicked pun is common among medical men: "Five minutes with Venus may mean a lifetime with Mercury," a specimen of sardonic jesting with death that so appeals to many doctors, however kindly and serious they may really be.

In no way can we better trace his degeneration than in his treatment of his wives; so I propose to describe it alone of all his innumerable misdeeds.

Firstly, it is a great mistake to suppose that

---

[2] According to Professor J. J. Welsh many ointments in use at the time contained mercury.

the only nervous result of syphilis is general paralysis. Among neurotic people it may cause serious mental troubles although it may not affect the actual brain-tissue so far as we can see with a microscope. As this is perhaps not generally known, I quote a sentence from the *Oxford Textbook of the Practice of Medicine*, by various authors, published in 1922. "Such patients are generally psychasthenic, ill-balanced and degenerate." The writer is speaking of the effects of syphilis upon mental diseases, and its propensity to cause "phobias" and "obsessions."

His first wife was Catherine of Aragon, who was some six years older than himself. After a fierce struggle with the pope the obliging Archbishop Cranmer pronounced a divorce between them. Martin Hume considers that this was entirely for personal reasons, because she had lost her personal charms, and because Henry had fallen in love with Anne Boleyn. Probably there was a great deal of the personal element in it, and it is quite possible that if Catherine had been willing to go into a convent and leave her husband to another woman—he actually proposed that the pope should allow him two wives—there might not have been the divorce that has been fruitful of such stupendous results for England. Catherine seems to have been a woman much under the influence of Spanish religiosity, and undoubtedly put up a strenuous fight to keep her husband; as was only right and proper. Probably the real degeneration in the king was yet to come; the spirochæte was still biding its time.

Since there seems to be a good deal of doubt about the exact dates of the famous premature births of Catherine, I give from Professor Pollard her actual record. On January 31st, 1510, seven months after marriage, she gave birth to a daughter still-born. Eleven months later, on January 1st, 1511, there was a son, who died in three days, as is still said because of the inordinate length of his christening. In September, 1513, there was another son, who was either still-born, or died immediately after it was born. In June, 1514, there was yet another son, but he, too, was no sooner christened than dead. Then, on February 18th, 1516, came the little Princess who, being born to misery, became "Bloody Mary." Then, in 1517 "it is probable that there were several miscarriages." On November 18th, 1518, came the last of the unhappy woman's efforts. It was a boy and still-born. And Catherine was by now forty years of age and obviously could have no more children. She had done her best, poor lady, but found her husband's spirochætes too much for her.

General experience is that the tendency in constitutional syphilis is to cause a string of prematurely born children or miscarriages; then a child born at full time, but showing evidences of disease; then, the tendency having worn itself out, one or more backward but seemingly healthy children. But, after Mary was born, apparently the tendency still remained. Probably local internal trouble still persisted in Catherine, and she had not entirely worn out the infection. Undoubtedly a good modern surgeon would have cured her and altered the history of England. That the stout-hearted daughter of Ferdinand and Isabella actually died of the syphilis which she had probably gained from her husband would appear to be shown by the account of the post-mortem examination which was secretly held by a man who was trying to prove that Henry VIII had poisoned her. He reported after getting the body ready for embalming, that she was all sound but the heart, which was "black and hideous, with a black excrescence which clung closely to the outside." Doubtless this represented an aortic aneurysm, which is known to be a common result of untreated syphilis. I know that the findings have been attributed to cancer of the heart; but cancer of the heart is so rare, if it ever occurs, while aneurysm is so common, that I prefer the interpretation here given.

I regret that my little essay on Henry's second wife, Anne Boleyn, has been much misunderstood by readers of *Post Mortem*. The view I there took was that if the stories about her were true they could only be explained by the supposition that she was suffering from nymphomania. Nymphomania does not necessarily imply that a girl is of abandoned character; it is a pathological condition of the nervous system. To this day it sometimes comes on after childbirth, especially if accompanied by terror and anxiety. It is in these women part of the Curse of Eve.[3] It may happen to any woman, and sometimes causes scandal before it is discovered. What circumstances could be imagined more terrible than those in which the tragic second queen found herself.

Henry had married her in hopes of gaining a son and heir in spite of the curse which people believed lay upon him for the multifarious premature births of her predecessor, or rather for the mortal sin of marrying his deceased brother's wife.

[3] In cases resembling nymphomania that occur after childbirth we call it puerperal insanity.

Still further to complicate the matter, Catherine of Aragon had sworn that she had never had connection with the dead Prince Arthur at all. Truly the whole thing becomes more and more complex as we gaze. A canon law which looked upon a carnal act as a deed which must be sanctified by God whenever it was performed, either before or after marriage; a girl who desired to be queen; another older woman who fought fiercely for her rights as both wife and religious fanatic; a multitude of fierce partisans; racial, political, and religious animosities; over all a man enraged by "love," fear, and brutality. Who could get at the truth about poor little Anne's marriage? It is impossible; one can only sympathise with everybody, and try to understand.

As I said, if the stories are true they can only be explained on pathological grounds. What girl in her senses would go rushing about the Court soliciting promiscuously in the manner of which Anne is accused? Mr. Philip W. Sergeant has written a book to prove that all the stories are really based upon slanders set agoing by Chapuys, ambassador of Charles V; and it was to fierce religious and political animosity that Anne owed her bad reputation. According to him she was really a rather vindictive, free-spoken woman, a great worker with her hands, fond of dress, musical, and passionately fond of dancing. This is a new outlook on the Anne of Froude and most historians, but is confirmed by several known facts. For instance, some of her laborious needlework is said to be still preserved in Hampton Court Palace. I have not seen it, for it is many years since I was at that palace; but it must be very sad to gaze upon it and think how tragic was the fate of Mr. Sergeant's dancing, singing, industrious little queen.

Another thing upon further reflection rather casts doubt even on the pathological explanation. Froude accused her of soliciting Sir Henry Norreys after the birth of Elizabeth—if I remember rightly, it was less than three weeks afterwards. Is it conceivable that Sir Henry Norreys would be allowed alone into Her Majesty's sick-room only three weeks after the greatest event of any woman's life—the birth of her first-born?

A lady who claims to be an Irish descendant of that George Boleyn who was accused of adultery and incest with Anne has written a long and interesting letter concerning her family and Anne in particular. Narrating the family traditions—and, as she says, family traditions must always be accorded great value—she tells me that the descendants of George Boleyn hold strongly that Anne may have been a gay little flirt, but that there was never anything really morally wrong with her; and that the whole accusation was in her own words—she is an American—a "frame-up" on the part of Henry VIII and Thomas Cromwell. Quite possibly, therefore, Anne may really have given nothing more than nods and becks and wreathed smiles to the men who were accused of adultery with her; possibly even the musician, Mark Smeaton, may have had his confession wrung out of him entirely by torture and by Cromwell's terrible personality.

The truth about her burial seems to be that she was not bundled into a cask as I heard from one of the caretakers at the Tower, but that she was hurriedly put into a partly filled box of arrows. According to Mr. Sergeant they dug up the box in 1876 and found her delicate skeleton, with slender bones and severed neck. It is all very tragic and very sad. The difficulty is that Cromwell seems to have taken care that all the evidence in her favour perished. We do not hear from her friends.

It was apparently during Queen Anne Boleyn's reign that the first appearance began of that frightful physical degeneration in the King which so impressed all his contemporaries; and it was probably from that circumstance that Anne gained the discredit of being the great prime mover in his degeneration; it was not fair of Mr. P. C. Yorke, in the *Encyclopædia Britannica*, to say that she appealed only to his lower nature. Some woman when he was about fourteen had done so most effectually, and years later Anne had to suffer for it. He probably appealed to Anne through his music, for he was a skilled musician, and one of the anthems which he wrote is still performed in English cathedrals.

There are still one or two things to remark when dealing with Anne Boleyn. First of all there was the birth of Elizabeth when she expected and fervently prayed for a son; secondly, the next was a miscarriage, said to have been brought on by seeing Jane Seymour sitting on her husband's knee; another account is that it was a son prematurely born through anxiety because of a fall that he had when riding. Again these premature births! One would have thought that the constitutional syphilis in Henry VIII must have long worn itself out by that time!

Last of all we must glance at the conduct of the very obliging Archbishop Cranmer. He pronounced the decree of divorce—which, by the way, neither Catherine nor Henry himself ever seems to have recognised. Then he was present when Anne and Henry were married secretly. Then, when Anne, looking upon him as a friend, appealed to him in her desperate trouble at the end, he sent her a non-committal answer. As Mr. Sergeant dryly comments, it has only recently been proposed that this obliging man be made a saint of the Anglican Church.

There can be little doubt of the reason why Henry married Jane Seymour. Before he got Anne put out of harm's way he had fallen in love, as he called it, with Jane; and the Seymours, being very powerful people who, observing that the king's passions were already all-powerful with him (owing to his illness), took advantage of them to see that he married the new star, simply for the sake of their own particular sect, which happened to be Catholic. Here we see at once the fact that Henry, who thought himself so strong, was in reality already at the mercy of party politics.

Jane Seymour seems to have been a nondescript sort of woman, gentle and harmless. At the end of about a year she was delivered of the little son who, because his father's syphilis had seemingly worn itself out, passed through the perils of his infancy only to die ultimately of what looks very much like pulmonary tuberculosis, the other curse of the Tudors. Childbirth killed the colourless Jane Seymour, undoubtedly through puerperal septicæmia, though once again the cock-and-bull story of an overlong christening has been revived.

Next came Anne of Cleves, the famous "great Flanders mare" of legendary reputation, of whom we have all learned at school. Again, according to Major Hume, Henry was so worked upon by his political advisers that he for once made an utter fool of himself, and married a picture by Holbein procured by Thomas Cromwell. In recommending this marriage Cromwell took a great risk, for, as is well known, no man can select either wife, pipe or hat for another. It is said that Henry had proposed to the French ambassador that he should hold a sort of Babylonian marriage-market among the damsels of France, whence he should select the prettiest; but it is also said, by Professor Pollard this time, that the Frenchman made such an answer that for the only recorded time in his life, Henry was seen to blush. It is difficult to imagine such a jape—even if French— as would make Henry Tudor blush.

The important thing to tell about Anne of

Cleves is that Henry, having passed several nights in her room, proclaimed that he had discovered that she was not *virgo intacta*. There are also several indecent stories that he was said to have related of her, but as they are not entirely germane to my present object, and as I do not wish this to be a mere *chronique scandaleuse* I omit them.

While he was thus uncertain, being almost in the position of Hajji Baba when he discovered that he had married a veiled woman who turned out to be excessively plain, Henry again strove for freedom. He secured it by simply repudiating his bride on the Euripidean method of "it was my tongue that swore," not my soul. Anne seems to have been a good-natured sort of German frau who accepted the inevitable with a good grace, and doubtless she was not sorry to be left alone with her knitting. Henry gave her £4,000 a year and two country houses, and called her his sister. She was not above cracking a risky joke with her temporary husband when he became still more prodigious as to his size and gluttony. It was while he was worried about Anne that Luther announced that Squire Harry thought himself to be God.

Lady Catherine Howard was the most pitiful of all, as Anne Boleyn was the most tragic. Once again there was the inevitable see-saw of politics; Henry had got rid of Thomas Cromwell the Protestant by the simple method of cutting off his head in circumstances of unusual brutality even for the sixteenth century; and once more the Roman Catholics came on top. The result was the sacrifice of pretty Catherine Howard. That she was by far the best looking of all Henry's wives can hardly be denied. Nobody looking at her gentle and thoughtful little face in the portrait that hangs in the National Portrait Gallery would ever dream that she was so immoral as people tried to prove. Her eyes were hazel, her hair was auburn; and she looks as virginal as though she had never been near the Court. Yet she was said to have had entanglements with at least three men. She had had a very unhappy childhood, and received due thrashings from her aunt the Duchess of Norfolk when that lady took a fancy to bestow them; but little education. She had no maternal supervision to keep her on the straight and narrow path in that sinful Court. Her music master, Mannock, boasted that she had promised to be his mistress; a kinsman named Dereham said that she was his wife; and she was reported to be engaged to her cousin, Culpepper. And now she was bestowed upon this new and

dreadful suitor, His Gracious Majesty [4] himself.
No wonder that Martin Hume became almost
dithyrambic about it. Indeed, Catherine Howard
had a hard fate.

I quote directly from Professor Pollard, who
mercifully glosses over the piteous details. "Rumours of Catherine Howard's past indiscretions
had at length reached the ears of the privy council. . . . Twenty-four hours later Cranmer put in
his hands the evidence of the queen's misconduct.
Henry refused to believe it in the rude awakening
from his dreams; he ordered a strict investigation
to be made. Its results left no room for doubt.
Dereham confessed his intercourse; Mannock admitted having taken liberties; and finally the
queen herself confessed her guilt. The king was
overwhelmed with grief and vexation, and shed
bitter tears. He offered his wife a pardon and
she might have escaped with nothing worse than
a divorce had not proofs come to hand of her misconduct with Culpepper during Henry's recent
absence in the north. This offence was high trea-
son and could not be covered by Henry's pardon
for her prenuptial immorality." Henry feared
lest the blood royal be contaminated. In Jan-

[4] The title was only recent. Formerly he had been called
"His Grace."

uary, 1542, Parliament considerately relieved this blubbering and neurotic man of his responsibility by "passing an Act of Attainder directed against his new wife, which, to save him pain, was signed by a Commission in his stead. Catherine declined his permission to go down to the house of Parliament and defend herself in person." In due course she was beheaded in the Tower. The story is that she said, "I had rather die a Culpepper than live a Queen." Doubtless in confessing at the back of her mind was the thought that it were better to be dead than to be married to King Henry VIII at the moment that his mental syphilis was approximating to its greatest terrors with all its obsessions and phobias. Seemingly the Parliament of England was not always so brave as we now think it to be. But if he knew so much about women as he had professed in the case of his repudiation of Anne of Cleves, why had he not applied his knowledge to the case of Catherine Howard before?

It seems a reasonable thing to glance at the other symptoms of syphilis that occurred at the time during the reign of Catherine Howard when his greatest degeneracy was coming on.

The ulcer on his leg sometimes closed, and the pain was so intense that he sometimes became

speechless with agony and went black in the face.[5]
He grew more and more corpulent every day.
When he went on progress to the north he cleared
the Tower by issuing orders that every prisoner
in it was to be beheaded. If these in an absolute
monarch are not symptoms of syphilitic psychasthenia, of a frightful moral and physical degeneration, what are they? Symptoms of whooping-
cough, perhaps!

Next and last came Catherine Parr, who was
said to have been degraded to the royal bed by
the Protestants to gain their own ends. She must
have been a brave woman to tackle the task of
nursing this man, whose temper by that time was
like that of a wild beast owing to his obsessions
and phobias. She was no beauty; she was short in
stature, but gifted with amazing tact. She had
already been twice a widow, so evidently she
thought she understood the art of nursing and
managing men, even such a man as her new husband. She is said to have been at the time in
love with Sir Thomas Seymour, whom she married after Henry's death, only to die in a short
time of puerperal fever. She reconciled Henry
to his daughter, Elizabeth, and is said to have
kept the peace between her and the Princess Mary.

[5] See how neurotic he was at the time!

71

We are told that she once had a theological dispute with the king; a risky thing to do. "A good hearing it is," said Henry, "when women become such clerks; and a fine thing it is to be taught in mine old days by my wife." Catherine explained that what she had said was merely intended to "minister talk"; so Henry answered, "Is it so, sweetheart; then we are friends again," and when Lord Chancellor Wriothesley came to arrest her Henry called him beast, knave and fool. She must indeed have been a remarkably clever woman, whatever her religious opinions.

As to his death it is quite impossible to get at the real truth. He had sent the Duke of Norfolk to the Tower and had ordered his execution to be fixed for February 28th, 1546. But, alas, on the 27th Henry lay dying. The exact details are so squabbled over for purposes of sectarianism, that it is impossible to distinguish between truth and falsehood. It is said on the one side that he died in an agony of conscience; on the other that Archbishop Cranmer came to ask him to give some token of his belief in Jesus Christ. The king is said to have roused himself from his stupor and pressed Cranmer's hand. While there are not sufficient details to offer an opinion it is possible that his stupor was uræmic, due to the slow degeneration of his kidneys during the many years that his body and mind had been degenerating. But one would prefer to have some independent authority for the statement that the dying man understood sufficient of what Cranmer was saying to him to press his hand at the mention of the blessed name of Christ.

To the best of my ability and in accordance with the best modern historical knowledge, I have drawn as honestly as I can the true character of Henry VIII, Defender of the Faith, as seen by a doctor. There are many stories told about him that I purposely have omitted from fear of being accused of exaggeration. But the general atmosphere of lust, obscenity, grandiose ideas, such as were noticed by Luther, and violence combined with cowardice, especially about disease, is all very typical of syphilis; one might almost call it diagnostic. He never became an indecent honest lunatic such as Ivan the Terrible, for ingenious historians who know the exact circumstances so far as anybody can know them at this time of day, are still able to find logical reasons for even the most dreadful of his actions. He did not become terrible; he became loathsome. To use the words of a witty journalist friend of mine he was not Henry the Terrible; he was Henry the Horrible.

He is the one man who ever disproved Shakespeare's vaunt:

> "This England never did nor never shall
> Lie at the proud feet of a conqueror."

For if England did not lie at the proud and probably dropsical feet of this obsessional syphilitic with doubtless a gigantic blood-pressure to add to his bad temper, words have no meaning.

The whole conduct of the English people throughout the Reformation is a beautiful example of the working of Dr. Wilfrid Trotter's herd instinct. Like a swarm of bees England swept this way and that, uncertain how to fly, looking for a resting-place where it might start the new era just as the swarm searches for a place to start a new hive; and then, suddenly, with no obvious reason, darts upon its way, upon the usual English way of a compromise which doubtfully satisfies the strongest party.

It adds to the remark of R. L. Stevenson's cynical old Frenchman: "The English are a stupid people who have sometimes blundered into good."

How many men lost their lives owing to Henry's syphilitic obsessions and phobias it is quite impossible to say. The comparatively slight

74

derangement of judgment in those tyrannical times may have meant the block for scores. Perhaps when Sir Thomas More said, "Her Majesty Queen Anne Boleyn may dance and sing but her turn may still shortly come," the acutest mind in England perceived that his king was not entirely normal in mind.

Henry VIII was never a despot. If the law did not allow him to do as he wished, he simply got Parliament to alter it for him.

Edward VI

THIS poor little boy, in whom all the tragedy of the Tudors seems to have concentrated itself, was born to Henry VIII and Queen Jane Seymour in 1537. Henry had already forgiven himself for his conduct to Anne Boleyn, and was deeply attached to his new queen; during the progress of the christening he sat by the side of his wife and held her hand in order that she might not be too exhausted by the strain. She, poor thing, had to wear a great gown of ermine, and to sit upright on a state pallet to welcome and bless her little son as the service terminated. But her loving arms could not save him; already within him were implanted the seeds of death, a tuberculous tendency from his grandfather, Henry VII, and actual spirochætes from his father, Henry VIII. And, as Queen Jane clutched him to her bosom, she herself began to shiver; no doubt she thought her shivering was from fear lest she lose her son; but within a week of his birth she lay dead, probably from puerperal septicæmia. Henry was heart-broken; but at least the curse of

the Church had been lifted; he could now honestly
say that he had begotten a legitimate and living
son, and that the succession of the English throne
was safe. Where the brilliant little Anne Boleyn
had failed, this commonplace and featureless
Queen Jane, so colourless that everybody liked
her, or at least did not hate her, had succeeded.
So she being dead, Henry at once communicated
with the Court of France in order to get him another wife, if possible; that the Pope might see
how impotent he was to affect human destiny.
This was not because he was incurably lustful,
but because it was still important to have another
heir, should little Edward turn sick and die. Already, one thinks, the English Prometheus was
scaling Olympus with determined, though en-
grossed, footsteps; already Zeus might well
tremble at the ponderous footfalls of this fat and
syphilitic man.

But little Edward did not seem likely to die;
for, to all appearances he was a strong and healthy
little boy. If the Court of England had purposely meant to deny that Edward was syphilitic
it could not have chosen better words to do it in,
for, as the message announcing the glad news of
his progress said, "he sucketh like a child of
puissance." In the typical infantile hereditary

syphilis the baby suffers from "snuffles," and its
sucking powers are, to say the least, inadequate.
But the spirochæte has other ways of taking its
revenge upon its host. It may lie latent for years,
and so poison the child's resisting powers that he
falls an easy victim to some deadly bacterium.
In the case of little Edward it seems to have been
the tubercle bacillus that first seized upon its
chance; and when, fifteen years later, just after
puberty, it was working its deadly will upon him
the spirochæte of syphilis joined the assault.

Edward was an affectionate little boy, of good
impulses. Of course it was unthinkable that a
prince should ever be flogged; so the fond father
appointed a whipping-boy to act vicariously in his
stead. It was Barnaby Fitzpatrick who was honoured by receiving the royal thrashings, though
Edward was such a good little boy that Barnaby
was seldom called upon for duty, and grew up a
firm friend of the little king who might have suffered in his person but for him. Edward's wet-
nurse was a motherly woman whom he later called
his "mother-jak." I do not know what childish
utterance that may have represented, but it is silly
enough a term to have come from the mouths of
babes and sucklings. At eleven months old no less
a personage than Thomas Cromwell visited him

officially and, no doubt, dandled him upon his knee. Says Cromwell's secretary, speaking of this time, "And I do assure your lordship that I never saw so goodly a child of his age; so merry, so good and loving a countenance, and so earnest an eye, as it were exercising a judgment towards every person who repaireth to his grace; and, as it seemeth to me, his grace encreaseth well in the air where he is." (Already he had been sent to the country for his health.) "And, albeit a little of his grace's flesh decayeth, yet he shooteth out in length and waxeth firm and stiff and he can steadfastly stand." So clearly he was a nice little boy of eleven months, if anything rather forward for his age.

When he was about two, his father, the king, used to take his little son in his arms and stand at the window to show the multitude how bravely his boy was fighting life; and the crowd would clap and cheer for joy, for King Henry VIII was still beloved, and the Tudor succession was at every Englishman's heart; the awful mental and physical degeneration in the king was still to come, and there is no more delightful scene in Henry VIII's life than that of him standing at the window holding up his son to be cheered by the crowd. How little we really know of our public men!

Who could have foretold that this smiling king was to become the most murderous tyrant who ever sat upon the throne of England? For the present let him be glad, and his little son with him, smiling and chuckling with true Tudor tact. The tragedy to both comes soon enough.

Some time before this, the proud wet-nurse announced that her foster-child "has three teeth and a fourth appeareth." I cannot discover the exact age at which this announcement was made. It would be interesting to know whether his dentition was entirely normal; but probably little Edward seemed normal enough. When he came to be educated the amount of learning that was stuffed into that poor child's head was simply amazing—worthy of Elizabeth; worthy of bluff King Hal himself. He could speak both Latin and Greek; he habitually wrote in Latin, and could translate a Latin author into Attic Greek. For his friend he selected little Jane Dormer, a girl of his own age; the two ran about and played together. The two made a pretty picture, if you can forget the fate that was hanging over the little boy. He kept a journal, and a day came, April 2nd, 1552, when he noted "this day I fell sick of the measles and the smallpox." The young diagnostician must have been very sure of his insight. The fact that two dissimilar eruptions came out on the little boy at the same time rather seems to indicate that there was some other toxin at work, probably syphilitic.

As he grew up he began to show signs of both obstinacy and religiosity, which, with a little encouragement, might have become as fanatic as those of Mary Tudor herself and led to a real good old sixteenth-century religious persecution. It was perhaps fortunate for England that the clever little boy died before he could do any real mischief. We know a great deal about his actual death. For a long time his health had been failing; he was racked with a constant and incurable cough, and apparently showed all the symptoms of a rapid consumption. The regular doctors having failed to cure him, England's Majesty was entrusted to the care of a woman who professed to have acquired possession of a cure-all. Under her treatment the king became rapidly worse. "His legs swelled, his complexion became sallow, his hair fell out; the terminal joints of his fingers fell off" (syphilitic dactylitis?). "Eruptions came out on his skin, and he lost his fingers." The luckless laundress who washed his shirts also suffered from terrible things; she lost her nails and the skin off her fingers, which gave rise to the suspicion that some one had been trying to poison the king her employer. But probably either she had been using some cheap soap or else she had syphilis herself. So, the quack having proved that her cure-all was doing the king more harm than good, was sent about her business, and the regular doctors were recalled. Froude thought that she had been using some mineral poison, and that in truth Edward VI had actually been poisoned by her, though not intentionally. As for me, I am quite prepared to believe that she had somehow got hold of a preparation of mercury which she was using on the light-hearted assumption, which was probably true, that in 1550 everybody was suffering from syphilis, and that when she tried it on Edward's form, already wasted and powerless by the long struggle with tuberculosis, the spirochætes that had been lying latent within him suddenly became active during the "storms of puberty" with the terrifying results that we have just seen. Possibly the woman may have bragged of her discovery about mercury; and everybody would at once say, "See what you are doing to our beloved young king with your mineral poisons!" There is much virtue in a name. Call mercury a "mineral poison," and it is at once damned as much as if you had called it a "drug." But vegetable poisons are far worse than mineral poisons; yet nobody dreams of saying that we should not take strychnine to "buck us up," nor morphine to relieve us of intolerable pain. Probably it was that woman's hard luck that she tried mercury at the very moment when the king's latent syphilis was about to come to the surface; and no doubt it was just such incidents as this which have given to mercury such a bad name, that the moment one prescribes it the patient always says, "Not mercury, doctor, please."

But that unfortunate woman was dismissed and the regular practitioners returned to their prey with the good old sixteenth-century remedies for coughs, which, if they could not cure, would certainly not bring the patient all out in a rash. The rumour went about that they were poisoning the king, that he was already dead. As young Edward lay gasping and coughing and sweating on his death-bed his attendants said to him that it would be wise for him to let himself be seen; so, with true Tudor sense of duty, he dragged himself to the window and looked out at the crowd waiting like ghouls to hear that he was dead. When they saw his face, grey, pinched and dying, the crowd cheered as it cheered when it saw him held up in his father's arms. Though some cheered, yet some held to it that a man who could look so ghastly must be dead, and indeed the rumour that he was dead was but confirmed by the sight of him.

His last prayer was "O Lord God, free me, I beseech you, from this calamitous life." What was that poor young lad doing that he had already begun to wonder why he had ever been born, as many men have wondered about themselves since him? Tuberculosis of the lungs is often accompanied by a sense of euphoria, that is to say, the patient does not feel so ill as he should feel. But syphilis of the lung is gloomy enough, and sometimes gives rise to symptoms indistinguishable from tuberculosis. On the whole, therefore, I might rather be inclined to hazard a guess that it was syphilis of the lung that killed little Edward VI. I grant that this guess might be based mainly on that sad prayer, coupled with all the other symptoms that I have narrated. Then, after he had been trying to look upon his subjects with eyes that probably saw nothing, he suddenly cried, "I faint—Lord, receive my soul," and fell back dead.

But is it not rather fantastic to summon either in particular of the two Earthly Twins, tubercle and syphilis, to the final assault, especially a manifestation of syphilis so rare as syphilis of the lung? These two form an alliance when it occurs that is not like the alliance of States; they do not quarrel, but never let go their grip until the patient dies. And it is in an alliance between delayed hereditary syphilis and pulmonary tuberculosis that we must probably seek for the death of Edward VI.

Probably it was lucky for him, and lucky for England that he died; and he did well by wondering why he was ever born. How much more violently would the wonder of life have shocked him when he came to learn how thorny is the path of a man who is too religious! *Sed Dis aliter visum.* It needed no inscrutable wisdom on the part of the Almighty to realise that Edward Tudor was "better dead."

Mary Tudor

I HAVE already discussed the character of this unhappy woman in *Post Mortem*. To the psychology that I there enunciated I have nothing to add; and I still believe that if she had not been for so long an old maid, if she had not been neglected by Philip II, or if she had been married, as she probably would have preferred, to Charles V, England would not have had occasion to call her "Bloody Mary." She but supplies another instance, if one were needed, that religion and sex [6] are not far apart.

For details as to her physical health I am indebted to the *British Medical Journal* for 1910, where there appeared that noteworthy series of articles on Royal Deathbeds which has been so useful to historically minded doctors.

As a child she was always sickly, though as she grew up she had to undergo the rigid mental discipline that Henry enforced on all his children. Being a very learned man himself, he naturally

[6] Please note that "sex" does *not* mean "sensuality."

tried to imbue them with his own hunger for knowledge; and all three rivalled their father in intellectual endeavour.

With better fortune, better health, and perhaps we might say with a less exacting father, Mary might have been as great as he. Instead her really great parts turned her into the road of tyranny and persecution, and "Bloody Mary" she will remain for all time.

The "storms of puberty" that had shattered the frail barque of Edward VI, and brought his latent spirochætes to the surface, beat hard upon Mary's body, and left her an embittered and sickly woman, with an intellect below her station, and a conscience above it. But what she mistook for the love of God—religion—was probably a love more fleshly; the desire of the moth for the star, as Shelley puts it poetically. Indeed, it is difficult to describe this primitive instinct in language that shall not be poetical; the great brain of man has idealised love until it is the emotion furthest from prose that humanity is capable of suffering; and that which is originally common to man and the brutes becomes the noblest feeling of the human brain; transcendental. And when again sublimated it may lead to the fiercest of injustices, to the most savage of religious persecutions. To that goal it led Mary Tudor, the most unhappy woman in English history.

As a girl she suffered from menstrual troubles that caused her great pain; her normal menstruation was often scanty; and this has been attributed to overstudy. To this day we find that any overstrain, or even a sudden change of climate, may cause amenorrhœa in a young woman; many of our English girl-immigrants, having left the depths of an English summer for the mildness of a Sydney winter, suddenly terrify their friends by becoming amenorrhœic, often to their unfounded mental distress. Later on she suffered from what she called her "old guest," of which the chief symptom was amenorrhœa. The probability is that soon after her marriage with Philip she really did become pregnant, and miscarried. The disappointment weighed heavily on her mind. Was it possible that she, who was so earnest, virtuous and religious, should be affected by the same curse as the wives of her father? She became cachectic— that is to say, her complexion assumed the ashy hue of a person dying of cancer; and her abdomen swelled as though she were again pregnant. Sir Spencer Wells in 1877 hazarded the guess that she probably suffered from "ovarian dropsy," an old-fashioned term for what we should now call "parovarian cyst," a tumour that takes its origin from a little body adjacent to the ovary, and, being distended with fluid, causes enormous swelling of the abdomen. It is the one abdominal tumour which, if tapped, may possibly not return, and the patient may be cured with no further ado.

For years before she died she had suffered from very bad health; she was never well, and could never attend to her work properly, owing to the terrible headaches that afflicted her; these were possibly due to her bad eyesight. With these also went palpitation of the heart. She never became old, for she died at forty-two; and most likely the proverb was as true with her as it still is with every young person—"If you feel your heart, it is not your heart; it is something else, generally your stomach."

It is quite true that she, like Charles V, felt the loss of Calais desperately; her exact words to her ladies-in-waiting were, "When I am opened you will find Calais lying on my heart." Probably the fluttering at her heart put the idea into her head; and equally probably that fluttering ultimately came from her pelvic distress, which in turn would doubtless cause indigestion. We often see similar cases to-day.

Her father had compelled her to sign a statement that his marriage with Catherine of Aragon had been "by God's law and man's incestuous and unlawful"; thereby forcing her to declare herself a bastard. The parliament of her brother Edward VI passed an Act of Uniformity that enjoined services in English and did not permit of the Mass. To Mary, as a devout Roman Catholic, this appeared to be a form of persecution. She therefore appealed to her cousin the Emperor who intervened on her behalf, as he had tried to intervene on behalf of her mother during the divorce. But this time he was more successful, for he threatened England with war unless Mary's freedom of worship was restored to her, and her right of hearing Mass in her own chapel after the old canons. It is easy to see that the great Tudor dictator was dead and that only a sick woman sat on his throne. But Mary seems to have had no approximately impartial adviser. Throughout her reign she had no one to help her but the Emperor, who, great as he was, could not be called impartial in those dreadful times.

She was by no means personally cruel; she was lenient to political prisoners and restored out of her own privy purse some of the monasteries which her father had robbed. When her tumour —if it was a tumour—returned, in 1557, she drew up a will in expectation of the dangers of child-birth. She added a codicil to this in October, 1558, which showed that she had abandoned all hope of children. Her husband had not returned to her after he had gone to Belgium to see Charles V abdicate, and the elderly wife at last saw that no child of hers was to govern England.

In 1558 she suffered from what was then called "the new burning ague," which is now thought to have been the influenza; in that year it was raging in England, killing thousands of people.

She died suddenly in November, 1558, in full possession of her mind, while she was hearing Mass in her own private chamber, a right that she had won after such bitter struggles. Although no post-mortem examination was held, it is generally thought that she died of an ovarian tumour, though that is not likely to be correct, because an ovarian tumour would not cause sudden death. Nor is there any record of any sickness that would cause a heart disease that might kill her suddenly, unless perhaps the influenza may have weakened her heart. I rather fancy that my own guess is correct as given in *Post Mortem* that she died of "degeneration of heart and arteries," not necessarily but probably syphilitic and inherited from her father.

Any doctor looking at the portrait of her wizened, lined, and prematurely aged face would probably say, "That woman must have been a hereditary syphilitic," especially if he knew the history of Henry VIII. I am surprised to see that in the actual record of her life there appears to be none of the usual symptoms of hereditary syphilis beyond the general ill-health that was hers all her days, poor creature. Doubtless the illness in her father was working itself out by the time that she was born.

But she was very short-sighted; and possibly, as Sir Clifford Allbutt points out, this may have been due to "interstitial keratitis," an affection of the cornea of the eye which is almost confined to hereditary syphilitics. So that in Mary also we see the effects of the "tragedy of the Tudors." I am certain that that wizened face must come from hereditary syphilis, because one of the first patients I ever had looked extraordinarily like Mary Tudor, and the swellings on her arms for which she consulted me melted rapidly under the influence of mercury. Her photograph lies in my desk to this day as a perfect illustration of delayed hereditary syphilis.

Queen Elizabeth

NO decent man would add to the slanders that have been passed upon this extraordinary woman, who stood at the head of the English nation when it was engaged in one of its fiercest struggles for very existence. These slanders are so numerous in quantity, but in quality so much alike, that they may all be summed up in one— slander against her sexual morality. Professor Chamberlin (2), evidently considering that the morals of a great queen of the sixteenth century should resemble those of a great queen of the nineteenth, spent many years in ascertaining the nature of the sicknesses from which she was said to have suffered. The farrago of somewhat quackish-sounding symptoms that he discovered has no meaning in modern medicine. She has been slandered quite enough, poor lady, and I for one shall not add anything to it. Rather than seek an explanation for the innumerable contemporary physiological slanders I propose to see whether they are possible.

They may be said to have been summed up by

the kindest, most gentle and most sympathetic of historians, Professor A. F. Pollard (1), whose immense industry and meticulous fairness will at once absolve him from any obvious conscious bias, sectarian or otherwise. Writing of her extraordinary juggling with her numerous suitors he says: "There is evidence that she had no option in the matter and that a physical defect precluded her from hopes of issue. On this supposition her conduct becomes intelligible, her irritation at parliamentary pressure on the subject pardonable, and her outburst on the news of Mary Stuart's motherhood a welcome sign of genuine feeling. Possibly there was a physical cause for Elizabeth's masculine mind and temper, and for the curious fact that no man lost his head over her as many did over Mary Queen of Scots. To judge from portraits, Mary was as handsome as her rival; but apparently Elizabeth had no feminine fascination, and even her extravagant addiction to the outward trappings of her sex may have been due to the absence or atrophy of deeper feminine feelings. The impossibility of marriage made her all the freer with her flirtations, and she carried some of them to lengths which scandalized a public unconscious of Elizabeth's real security."

To analyse such remarkable slanders as those

passed by Mary Queen of Scots (3), and many
years after Elizabeth's death by Ben Jonson (4)
in his tipsy tattling would need a paper more
suited for a gynæcological journal than for general
publication. Without emulating Ben by going
into unpleasant physical details I content myself
by saying that so far as I know there is *no* physical
defect of the female form obvious to the sufferer
which will preclude hope of offspring, and yet
allow her to reach the age of nearly seventy.
Before coming to that conclusion the author laid
down four postulates to himself [7] which will occur
to every critically minded doctor; and it seems to
him that every suggestion fails miserably in at
least one of these postulates. And since, when
tested in this way, every slander founded on the
physical appearance of her body necessarily fails,
it is equally possible that the suspicions thus based
may be equally without foundation. Such rumours about her are founded upon a lamentable

[7] These postulates are:

(*a*) Her supposed deformity must have been such as would
allow her terrible father and her anxious mother to accept her
as a daughter, although they both desperately longed for a son
and heir.

(*b*) It must have been such as would have been known to
herself.

(*c*) It could not have interfered with the ordinary physiological processes of her life.

(*d*) It must have been such as would not interfere with her
living in at least tolerable health to the age of sixty-nine.

want of knowledge of woman's physiological and anatomical necessities. (11)

It seems to me, that we can gather better evidence from contemporary portraits than from contemporary religious slanders; it is well known that whenever sixteenth-century religion came in at the door objective truth flew out at the window. No one can study the beautiful portrait of Queen Elizabeth which Miss Gwen John allows me to publish without thinking: "That is not the portrait of a loose woman! She may have been cruel, vindictive, merciless, but she cannot have been loose and sensual."

Her amazing personality is best explained by the new science of the ductless glands—endocrinology.[8] Sometimes she seems to have had all the male qualities, such as swearing, roughness of speech, freedom from convention. Sometimes she seems to have behaved like a doting old maid, in her inordinate love of dress, jewellery, and flattery. Rather than believe that she was abnormal in form, which I think to be impossible considering the known facts of her physiology, I find it easier to believe that in some way her "endocrine balance" was abnormal. It is now rather more than suspected that no individual is entirely male

[8] If it is a science.

or entirely female; the psychic qualities of both
sexes are more or less mingled in everybody, and
thus we could easily explain the remarkable fact
noted by Professor Pollard that no man ever seems
to have fallen in love with Elizabeth sufficiently
to risk his head for her. A century before, Owen
Tudor fell in love with Katherine of Valois (7),
and risked death by marrying her secretly. But
no such vehement lover appeared for Elizabeth;
and, if he had, her want of "endocrine balance"
would not have prevented her from child-bearing.
When she shouted to Sir Nicholas Throckmorton,
"God's death, villain, I'll have thy head," (3) the
violence of the male in her came to the surface;
when she fondled and fooled with the Duke of
Alençon and called him her "little frog" (6) and
other silly names, the doting old maid in her was
paramount. Major Hume considers that it was
with the Duke of Alençon that Elizabeth was in
love for the first and only time in her life; and it
is quite possible.

The only thing that my speculation does not
explain is the bitter cry from the heart that was
wrung from her when she heard of the birth of
King James I to her great rival, Mary Queen of
Scots: "The Queen of Scots is the lighter of a fair
son, but I am a barren stock!" (3) How did she

know? Was she thinking of the amazing number of miscarriages that befell two of her father's wives, which to us now appear such certain evidence that he was probably suffering from constitutional syphilis? That is the best suggestion I am able to make.

Innumerable attempts have been made to explain the slanders upon Queen Elizabeth, from Miss Gwen John's explanation given in her little play, "The Prince," (12) that probably they arose from accidental episodes that occurred when she was about her normal duties at Court, to Major Hume's idea—which is generally held—that they were the result of purposeful "hoaxing" by the Great Queen, all done for the sake of her country. True, like her father Henry VIII, Elizabeth was very patriotic; but, as one of Professor Chamberlin's doctors suggests, it is difficult to distinguish between her patriotism and her desire to keep her own head on her shoulders. So far as I know the present suggestion—that the contemporary rumours about her physical malformation were impossible—has never been put forward before. It again leaves the field open for those who are able to estimate the effects of sectarian enthusiasm upon the human mind to find some other explanation than a physical malformation.

Her character has been so much besmirched by slander that we are sometimes apt to forget that in reality she was as clever and intellectual as her great father in his youth. She knew several languages, and to seek consolation in the worries that necessarily befell her it is said that she translated Boëthius' "Consolatio Philosophiæ." (9)

If we are to remember her as the man-struck old maid who philandered with and petted her favourites, it is equally well for us to remember her as the intellectual woman who was able to translate a deep philosophical work. The extremely intellectual qualities that one finds in Elizabeth are sometimes forgotten in the whirlwind of sectarian slander and patriotism that had centred itself on her head. Possibly the reason why she fixed upon Boëthius for translation—he had already been done by Chaucer—is because he wrote his great "consolation" in prison while he was awaiting the Roman executioner. Perhaps she thought that his case somewhat resembled her own.

Her dual personality came out strongly in her last words. According to Sir Sidney Lee they were "Ad inferos eat melancholia"—"To hell with melancholy." Not long afterwards she fell into a deep coma (10)—probably caused by septic intoxication from an abscess in her tonsils, acting upon a woman whose arteries were much older than her years—and died in her sleep. In these words one sees the reckless courage that we suppose to be male, swearing and laughing in the face of death however unwelcome he may be, and the feminine desire to charm which led her to paint her face as she said them.

But after all, the best epitaph upon Elizabeth is the little verse that she scratched upon a windowpane at Woodstock Manor, where her loving sister Mary was "entertaining" her much as we entertained Napoleon at St. Helena:

"Much is suspected of me;
Nothing proved can be;
Elizabeth prisoner."

And perhaps it is as well that nothing can be proved against the personal morality of one of the greatest women in history. One imagines that her wraith would laugh ironically at all our vain efforts, as her young girlhood evidently laughed at poor Mary as she scratched the words *Elizabeth prisoner*. (5)

I take from the *British Medical Journal* of 1910 the description of her actual death, because it is in accordance with my own experience of the deaths of fierce and obstinate old ladies.

Lady Southwell, one of her maids of honour, said: "She kept her bed for fifteen dayes besides the three dayes that she sat upon her stool without speaking; until one day, being pulled upon her feet by force, she stood upon her feet for fifteen hours. Her Majestie understood that Mr. Secretarie Cecil had given forth that she was mad; and therefore in her sickness she said 'Cecill, know thou that I am not mad; you must not try to make Queen Jane of me.'" Queen Jane was "Crazy Jane," mother of Charles V, and this recollection of the days of her youth, when Charles V was the greatest man in the world, is very characteristic of an old person. "And," continues Lady Southwell, "though by Cecil's means many stories were spread about that she was mad, myself, nor anie that were about me, could never see that her speeches, soo well adapted, proved her distracted mind."

Then they lifted her into bed; she fell asleep; and the last of the great personal monarchs of England died in coma. There was no sectarian nonsense about her waking from a stupor to press anybody's hand, when all she wanted was to get on with her dying.

But though Elizabeth was so great and had such an astonishing effect on English history (8) it would be a mistake to turn her into the heroine of a sentimental novel.

(1) A. F. Pollard, *Political History of England*.

(2) F. Chamberlin, *Private Character of Queen Elizabeth*.

(3) F. Chamberlin, *The Sayings of Queen Elizabeth*.

(4) Ben Jonson, *Conversations with Drummond of Hawthornden*.

(5) F. A. Mumby, *Girlhood of Queen Elizabeth*.

(6) M. S. Hume, *Courtships of Queen Elizabeth*.

(7) Mabel Christie, *Henry VI*.

(8) Rachel Taylor, *Aspects of the Italian Renaissance*.

(9) *The Australasian Journal of Philosophy*, June, 1924.

(10) Facts from the *British Medical Journal*, 1910; guess my own.

(11) Julian Huxley, *Essays of a Biologist*.

(12) Gwen John, *The Prince*.

Ivan the Terrible

THE life of this criminal lunatic has been described so often, with so much journalistic horror, that I hesitate to offer the plain matter-of-fact comments of a doctor upon it.

In order to understand the Russia of the last few centuries, we must first of all glance at Russian history. Under the brutal yoke of the Mongols the Russians learned the worst extremes of cruelty to which the vanquished in an Oriental country must submit; for, their country laid waste by civil war and devastated by the Tartars, the whole people were familiar with bloodshed, misery and cruelty. A man's children were his slaves, whom he could sell four times, and his wife and family lay under a sterner rule of fatherhood than ever obtained even in Rome or in Asia. Prisoners of war had to sell themselves as slaves lest they starve.

Ivan was born in 1530, son of Vassili Ivanovitch and Helena Glinska. One of his brothers was an imbecile, and his father was sullen, changeable, and savagely ferocious.

When Ivan was three years of age his father died, and, under the regency of his mother his education in vice began; indeed, it seems to have been prodigious. Although Helena seems to have done her best to protect him, he was encouraged by courtiers to yield to every form of self-indulgent vice that is possible to a young man. He used to watch with delight his dogs as they fell upon prisoners whom he had had thrown to them; and was constantly suspicious of the Boyars, or aristocrats, whom he suspected to have organised conspiracies against him. It is said that they used to organise their conspiracies either in the name of Ivan or of his mother; and they were opposed by their natural enemies, the trading classes. Hence it was that Ivan conceived a violent hatred and terror of the Boyars, and an equally foolish trust in the merchants. He had to suffer many indignities, and saw his favourites murdered before his eyes. Ivan struck back, until at last he captured one Shousky, last of the Boyars, and gleefully threw him to the dogs from the balcony whence he had often seen his prisoners eaten. A great fire broke out in Moscow in 1547, when Ivan was seventeen years old; seventeen hundred people perished in the flames. The populace rose in fury, accusing his grandmother and her sons of setting Moscow ablaze. Being a good grandson Ivan acted with vigour; he did not try to ascertain how far the old lady and his uncles were guilty, but incontinently seized upon the ringleaders of the people and put them to death as they deserved. In the midst of the pother a monk—one Sylvester—appeared. He seems to have been like one of those Oriental prophets who are said to have dared to tell the truth to kings. Bravely facing Ivan, he foretold the future in many visions and dreams; and warned Ivan that it was owing to his own misdeeds that Russia was suffering such tragic torments.

For some reason Ivan spared him, called together a synod of priests and other intelligentsia of Russia and asked for its aid in the government. Flattered, the synod drew up rules for its ruler; and the next ten years are pictured to us— possibly by friends of the synod—as a veritable *quinquennium Neronis;* though the period was longer than Nero's. There was good government and outward prosperity; the army was reformed; a new code of laws was devised; a printing press was established; Archangel was founded; trade with England was set afoot through the White Sea; by victories in Livonia the frontier was pushed towards the Baltic; fortresses against the

Tartars were established in the Crimea; and the Turks were driven back. In these wars Ivan IV showed himself to be a great and able general; a worthy predecessor of that Peter the Great who was soon to come after him.

But this was too good to last. In 1552 his wife died: Anastasia, first of the Romanoffs, the woman, as it would now seem, who saved Russia by protecting the Tsar from harpies. Ivan was heart-broken. He suspected her to have been poisoned, as every sudden death in the sixteenth century was attributed to poison; and from a little village near Moscow he wrote a violent letter, accusing the Boyars both of poisoning his Anastasia and of misgoverning Russia during his minority. He concluded by threatening that God called him to abandon the ungrateful people, who were unworthy of such love as his.

This threw Russia into a panic. "How shall we get on without our ruler?" they asked. "Who will defend us against our enemies? What will the sheep do without their shepherd?"

Evidently Ivan was a politician of no mean order; he knew his Russia. Touched by the weeping of the herd, he returned to his subjects. But how changed an Ivan! Formerly he had been a splendid man physically, tall, broad-shouldered, with hawk nose and eagle eyes; a true tsar of the dynasty of Rurik; fit leader of the great Russian people. On his return to his loving people he was suddenly become thin and wasted; his hair was falling; his skin was dull; his eyes had lost their brilliance; physical degeneration had already set in.

Considering his subsequent history, it is probable that in the fit of petulance after the death of his beloved wife he had become infected with syphilis, which was then at the height of its conquering career throughout Europe. Eight days after her death he married a Circassian woman, who was of a rough mind, and of coarse breed; possibly it may have been from her that he caught his disease, for to her influence is generally attributed his mental degeneration.

Such a fate often happens to a physically strong young man who suddenly finds himself deprived of his helpmate; and it was a wise law of the Romans, that every Governor of a province must be married; if for no other reason than that a wife would protect him from the attacks of other women who might mean him less well than she.

When he was seventeen, he had proclaimed himself "Tsar," thus showing himself bolder than his predecessors, who had perforce to content themselves with the title of "Grand-Duke."

Now, in his new-found glory, with his new wife by his side, he raised for himself a bodyguard of 6,000 men, whom he called the Opritschnitza. These men rode through the countryside with besoms and dogs' skulls at their saddle-bows. The emblems were supposed to signify that they would sweep away and hunt down all enemies of the Tsar.

But the Boyars were still to be properly punished for their wickedness; there were a few left, and at least the children of the infamous brood survived and had to be brought to justice; so Ivan rode through the land from country-house to country-house at the head of his men, besoms, dogs' skulls, and all, slaying and burning; a right merry journey. Those whom he could not kill perished in the snow, and all Russia lay in terror of Æsop's "King Stork." Better had it been for Russia if the people had left him in his self-imposed quarantine, to recover in peace from his skin-syphilis before it had attacked his brain. For a man suddenly driven mad by securing absolute power, and worried by fighting, revenge, and murder, to rage desperately about the country instead of treating his syphilis even by the crude methods that were in vogue in the middle of the sixteenth century, was sheer madness. To this day we find that physical and mental rest, fresh air, and mercury, are the standbys in the treatment of syphilis, and quite probably it is less deadly to-day than it was in 1550.

It was the custom in Russia for the Tsar, when he wanted a wife, to collect all the most beautiful women from whom he should make his choice; and in 1570 he, in need of another wife, collected no less than 2,000 girls; them he kept in captivity for more than a year, treating them as he would, ruthlessly and relentlessly, a symptom truly characteristic of cerebral syphilis in a man untroubled by restraints, moral or legal. From these he chose another wife for himself and one for his son, that the great name of Ivan should not perish from the earth.

The shuddering remainder he bestowed on his courtiers, or sent home.

Cerebral syphilis is an extraordinary thing. Besides causing general paralysis, which is known positively to be syphilitic, the disease acts upon the arteries of the brain, and the symptoms that it causes seem to depend upon the areas of the brain that the diseased arteries supply. If the affected area is the front of the brain in which the

109

intellectual faculties are supposed to be, all the symptoms of violent mental irritation are caused. They may begin quite early in the disease, and may last for many years till the patient's death; much appears to depend upon whether the patient has been able to live a decent and quiet life. That in the case of Henry VIII his disease apparently led to nothing more monstrous than cutting off two of his wives' heads—possibly they deserved it—and to violent and murderous political activity, would rather seem to show that if he had had a chance of rest and treatment he might have been no worse a king than many others who have won fame and gratitude. At least he was a highly educated man who certainly meant well at first. Ivan from the beginning was little better than a brute, of shocking family history and evil impulses. In him it probably went far beyond the stage of mere syphilitic psychasthenia.[9]

Seven wives in all were his, so that he beat Henry's record by one. I suppose he showed the same miserable story of domestic unhappiness, but I have not been sufficiently interested to find out. Some of his letters are still extant, and they show all the signs of insanity, in their unwieldy length,

[9] Please do not look upon this as a diagnosis; all we say positively is that the spirochæte must have affected his mind.

their foolish cunning, their voluble avoidance of the main point, and their inconsequence. On the evidence of these lettters alone any two doctors to-day would "sign up" Ivan IV. To say that he became wildly sexual would be to understate the matter: he developed the morals of a satyr. This is all very characteristic of syphilitic insanity, whose victims often find its worst effects in an utter abandonment of sexual restraint. It is almost as if the disease, being often the result of impurity, revenges itself on the victim by accentuating the very incontinence which has caused it.

The rest of the story of Ivan the Terrible—it is strange that history has not yet called him Ivan the Great—is not very interesting, except for two shocking incidents that we shall relate in their turn. It is simply the record of a man with an Oriental mind, maddened by syphilis, abandoning himself to the most ruthless cruelty, experimenting as if to plumb the depths of human wickedness. It would be wearisome both to tell it and to read it, with all the senseless stabbings, the stamping on the feet of helpless menials, the red-hot pokers, the experiments in torture, the burnings, the infamy. Let us hold our noses and turn to historical facts of a broader interest.

A man, in order to curry favour with the Tsar,

wrote a private letter to the King of Poland accusing the great city of Novgorod of conspiring against its ruler. Ivan found it by a trick, possibly with the connivance of the writer. He held his peace, just as Henry VIII had remained silent when he first heard of the sin of Anne Boleyn. But, without a word to anybody, he collected an army of 15,000 men, whom he marched towards the doomed city, around which he erected a barricade of stakes that no one might enter or leave so as to escape the just punishment of an outraged Tsar. Then, for every day throughout a period of five weeks 500 to 1,000 of the citizens were led into his presence and put to death in all sorts of amusing ways; Ivan's cleverness in devising new ways of killing seems to have been really wonderful. So wicked was the city that neither man, woman, nor child was spared, until but a scanty few remained alive. This niggardly remainder he collected before him, and forced to pray for the beloved Tsar. Like many syphilitic lunatics he had long considered himself to be God.

Then his eldest son, Ivan, who had grown up very like himself in character, so that people were already looking into the future with forebodings, took offence at what the half-witted fellow thought to be his father's insult to his wife,

Helena. With a roar Ivan rushed upon his son, striking him on the head with a heavy staff shod with iron. Ivan the prince dropped insensible, and died in a few days. Tsar Ivan was shocked unutterably, did penance and for a time seemed to regain sanity in his grief for the loss of his bright boy. But only for a time; soon the old monotonous régime of insensate cruelty returned.

1584 was a great year for Ivan. Feeling rather unwell the brilliant idea struck him that a well-born English girl would just suit his whim; so he sent a special messenger to Queen Elizabeth to select him one, also to inform her that, should his mutinous subjects prove unruly he would honour England by seeking therein a sanctuary. Thrice happy England; sanctuary for so many politicians! Well might refugees from the Austrian troubles in 1848 seek her green fields for peace.

The Virgin Queen selected one of her maids of honour, Lady Mary Hastings, for this dishonour. The Earl of Huntingdon, Lady Mary's father, and Lady Mary herself, shuddered and protested at the thought of her marriage with this dreadful man, especially as Ivan's seventh wife was still alive, and he had blithely proposed to set her aside in favour of the fair English maid, as the wretched creature would not die, nor leave him single, nor allow him to poison her. But for once, at least, Elizabeth's heart conquered her head, and she did not press the match; it was too tragic even for the sixteenth century, so that no English girl graced Moscow any more than did Caliban marry Miranda.

But Death was still waiting, inexorably. No doubt Ivan had long forgotten the apparently trifling illness from which he had suffered after the death of his first wife, or rather soon after his second marriage, but it had not forgotten him. Nature never forgets and seldom forgives, as so many doctors have said about Life.

A frightful portent, a comet, appeared in the sky, and as Ivan saw its horrid tail the thought struck him that it had come to warn him of his death. All Russia was at once in a ferment. Soothsayers were summoned from all the ends of the Tsardom. No less than sixty were collected to save the life of the Tsar, that religious lunatic, who had thought himself to be God; but the best they could do was to promise him that he would not die until twelve days had elapsed. "It will be the worse for you if your promise holds good," said Ivan in a fury; and with that he made up his mind to slay the soothsayers if he should survive the twelve days. The wife of his surviving son, who was to succeed him as the half-imbecile Tsar Feodor—syphilis again!—came to comfort him in his terrors, that this mighty Tsar should not have to go down into the dark his hand unpressed by any woman's; but Ivan indecently assaulted her and she fled in terror. To the later Ivan every woman was less feminine than female.

The twelfth day dawned and Ivan prepared the scaffold for the execution of the soothsayers. He himself took what precautions occurred to his simple soul, and spent most of the day on a sofa playing draughts with one of his male favourites—surely the most harmless and safest of joys; surely Ivan could have done nothing better unless he had forestalled fate by a good course of mercury thirty years before! At last, just as Ivan was beginning to congratulate himself that he had beaten fate, beaten the comet and beaten the astrologers, and was glutting himself with the anticipation of his next merry jest, he suddenly choked, uttered a stifled cry and fell back dead. Fate and syphilis had won; the astrologers had predicted so accurately that their heads were even then trembling on their shoulders. What had happened? No doubt his syphilis had affected the aortic valve of his heart, as it frequently does to-day. The blood, instead of coursing on its orderly way throughout his body, had run back into his heart, which, being overfull of blood, had stopped; and in a moment Ivan the Terrible was dead. The people wept for him, as being the Tsar. "Such was the Tsar," sobbed an admirer. "Such as he was, God made him."

I do not ask you to suppose that I have diagnosed Ivan from any special knowledge of my own; the facts I have enumerated are all to be found in a book called *The Blot upon the Brain*, by the late Dr. W. W. Ireland, a once-celebrated alienist of Edinburgh, who, so far as I know, was the first to suggest that Ivan IV probably suffered from syphilis. I go further, and suggest that he probably suffered from diffuse cerebral syphilis and syphilis of the aortic valve, just as people do to this day.

Twenty years ago I read that syphilis was unusually widespread in Russia, and I have often wondered since 1917 whether that long ago epidemic can possibly have had anything to do with recent Russian politics.

Luther's Devil

THOSE people who find it difficult to suppose that God so loves man that He occasionally suspends the operation of the principle of the conservation of energy in order that He may interfere in purely human affairs on this tiny planet will also find it difficult to believe in a personal devil who roams the world seeking whom he may devour and haunting people. Yet Martin Luther, who started the movement that ultimately led the world back to science and reason, had no difficulty whatever in believing this nonsense, and an infinity of other nonsense that to us nowadays seems little short of stark staring crazydom. Surely the poor gentleman must have been deranged, one thinks. Not at all, for Luther had the evidence of his own senses that he was haunted. He heard the foul fiend whistle and roar in his ears; the devil so gripped his heart that Luther never knew that the next moment might not be his last; sometimes he would cause him to be so giddy that when quietly sitting at work Luther was forced to fall from his stool. What was the matter with Martin Luther?

To begin with, most assuredly he was never mad; at the most one could fairly say that, like most of the great leaders of thought, Luther was probably of the manic-depressive temperament, with that strange mixture of apparently insane egotism and gloomy pessimism that so marks people of that temperament. In his famous prayer he orders his God about in a way that one can only compare to that of the Presbyterian divine who cried in a moment of irritation, "Noo, Lord, that's fair ridic'lous." If you read Luther's *Table-talk*, you will at once be struck with his curious temperament, which could combine a certain amount of shrewd common sense, such as you would expect from a man of Saxon peasant stock, with profound belief in the supernatural, a good deal of disbelief in his fellow-man, virulent hatred of the Pope and all his works, and a good deal of what looks uncommonly like sheer mysticism. *En passant* I found therein the solution of a problem that has long puzzled me. What was the mysterious "sin against the Holy Ghost" that nobody seems to understand? Let Luther explain it to us himself. Many persons have imagined that it represented one of those sexual perversions against which primitive races have so often launched a fierce tabu, simply because they knew nothing of sexual pathology. But really, according to Luther, it was nothing of the kind.

"Sins against the Holy Ghost are: first, presumption; second, despair; third, opposition to and condemnation of the known truth; fourth, not to wish well but to grudge one's brother and neighbour the grace of God; fifth, to be hardened; sixth, to be impenitent."

The only fault one has to find with this is that Luther does not tell us how to recognise the truth when one sees it. What *is* the criterion of truth? Otherwise it would seem to be a fairly good description of a certain type of neurasthenia. Many neurasthenics must go in mortal sin every day of their lives, for it is well known that the devil is particularly on the lookout for sins against the Holy Ghost.

Probably Luther's devil merely represented symptoms due to his wretched health. There is an excellent description of his dystrophy in Hartmann and Grisar's monumental *Life of Luther*, and Dr. Cabanes went over it again from the point of view of modern medicine; while nearly fifty years ago Dr. W. W. Ireland of Edinburgh reviewed it from the point of view of an alienist of that time. But Ireland did not perceive the immense influence of Luther's physical ailments on his mental condition.   How could you expect him to, fifty years ago?   From these three sources, therefore, I draw the material for this essay.   A précis of Dr. Cabanes' essay appeared in the *St. Louis Urologic and Cutaneous Review* for November, 1924.

Those fanatic Protestants who still believe that Luther was a meek and mild sort of monk who was driven to revolt by the sins of the "Whore of Babylon" should read his *Table-talk* in order that they may learn what manner of man he really was; and it will be surprising if they rise from it without an insight into Luther's character that may possibly change their whole conception of the Reformation.   Far from being a gentle and Christlike son of the Church, he was, so far as I can gather from his own words, perhaps the most frenzied theologian of that dark century of theologians.   In sheer outrageous superstition he could outdistance even the most ignorant peasant; his fear of the devil amounted to possession, because he attributed to the action of the foul fiend every single thing that he could not understand. An hour spent in reading Luther's *Table-talk* gives a better insight into the mind of man during that most terrible of all centuries than a year spent in reading an ordinary history.   The most reasonable excuse that we can make for him is that he was ill during the greater part of his life, suffering from one of the most distressing of all ailments.

From about the age of thirty he suffered from dreadful noises in the head, banging, whistling, thumping, and crashing. These were accompanied by terrible attacks of giddiness, which sometimes actually caused him to fall from his stool, and rendered work impossible. Towards middle life he became so neurasthenic that his mental condition became almost that of a lunatic —and indeed the Catholics did not miss the opportunity to say that he had actually become mad; but probably this was but a tit for Luther's own tat of extraordinary theological violence, and was certainly never true. But what is true is that he began to suffer from pains in the region of the heart, accompanied by a sense of dreadful oppression, so that sometimes he thought himself to be dying. As he grew older he became very deaf, and his cardiac distress became still more terrible.

All these things were to Luther certain evidence that his personal devil was attacking him; it is said that once he threw a pot of ink at the fiend, and the marks of it are still shown. All these things can be explained easily—as Dr. Cabanes suggested—if we suppose that Luther was suffering from Ménière's disease of the labyrinth, a disease of the inner ear that occasionally attacks middle-aged and gouty people, and is supposed to have added its tragedy to Dean Swift's already tragic life. The labyrinth is composed of the semi-circular canals, structures which are directed longitudinally and laterally to the axis of the body, and assist us in maintaining our equilibrium; if anything goes wrong in these tiny tubes an unconquerable feeling of giddiness overwhelms us, and it is thought that it is the washing this way and that of the fluid in these canals that causes the deathly feeling of giddiness in seasickness. And the fact that Luther's deafness steadily increased as he grew older seems to show that it was really caused by Ménière's disease. In 1541 he seems to have suffered from middle-ear disease, accompanied by dreadful earaches and discharge from the ear; while this lasted he became temporarily quite deaf, but all the time the labyrinthine disorder was going on.

Although he never seems actually to have suffered from gout, there seems to be no doubt that he was of the gouty diathesis, and that uric acid was constantly circulating in his blood, which, added to his manic-depressive temperament, would undoubtedly increase his tendency to gloom. If there can be any worse devil than frightful noises in the head, neurasthenia and uric acid in the blood, it would be interesting to learn what it is. Many a man has been driven to suicide by nothing worse. That Luther seems to have resisted any temptation to suicide that he may have had, speaks volumes for the strength of his purpose.

Probably the pains in his heart and accompanying fear of death represented a gigantic rise in his blood-pressure that would naturally occur in a man of such furious polemic zeal. And it may be that it possibly went so far as to cause angina pectoris. The accompanying fear of death certainly looks like angina, for there is no disease more frightful than angina; the patient feels as though the very grave were yawning for him.

Luther seems to have ultimately become on almost friendly terms with his devil. One night at the castle of Wartburg he heard a dreadful noise on the stair which woke him up—probably it represented noises in his own ears. He got out of bed in a rage with the insolent fiend.

"Is that thou, devil?" he shouted, but Satan said not a word. Then Luther, seeing that Auld Hornie was not to be drawn, got back into bed, piously commended himself to the care of the Lord Jesus Christ, and ultimately got off to sleep again. And this is the sort of thing that went on day and night with the Reformer. What a difference a course of salicylates and bromides might have made to Luther, and possibly through him to the whole Reformation, for there can be little doubt that Luther's devil played a great part in spurring him to yet more furious religious zeal. Sometimes even he began to despair, and admitted that it was impossible to make peace with the Pope so long as the papacy was the papacy and Luther was Luther. Viewed in this light, that in a sense he was Athanasius *contra mundum*, Luther's dictatorial and egotistical prayer to his God becomes almost pathetic, for he felt himself alone on the side of God against the mighty power whom he frankly calls anti-Christ, with hardly a soul helping him; it may have been during those passionate appeals to God for guidance before he made the break that his blood-pressure began to rise, for nothing causes the blood-pressure to rise like passionate emotion of any kind. Perhaps forty years later it killed him. Rising blood-pressure kills with exceeding slowness; let excitable politicians beware, for the same rules apply to them to-day as applied to poor Martin Luther, who was really less a man of God than a most furious politician.

Both Hartmann and Grisar and Dr. Cabanes give substantially the same accounts of his sudden death; so probably it is assured in spite of the Catholic story that he committed suicide. For two years a stone in the bladder had added to the tortures of his Ménière's disease, and on February 17th, 1546, his last seizure attacked him. While at Eisleben he became very restless. "Here at this little village I was baptised," he said. "It may be that I shall remain here." In the evening he felt that oppression in the chest of which he had so often complained, so he got his attendants to rub him down with hot flannels, and as soon as he felt better sat down to a light supper. In the middle of the night he awoke, feeling deadly ill. "O my God," he said, "I do feel so ill; I feel as though I were dying," and complained of a terrible oppression in his chest. His doctors found him bathed in a cold sweat and without perceptible pulse. He murmured his favourite text from St. John, "God so loved the world that He gave his only begotten son that whosoever believeth in him shall not perish, but shall have life everlasting." Then he became unconscious and his friends shouted into his deaf ears the question whether he remained steadfast in his faith in Christ and his doctrine, to which they thought they heard him say "Yes," though probably he did not hear them. At three in the morning his breathing suddenly became audible, and after a deep sigh he died. Probably this is a true account, for we often see the breathing of a dying man assume the up and down character that we call "Cheyne-Stokes."

For some extraordinary reason Messrs. Hartmann and Grisar attributed this obvious death from heart-failure to apoplexy. One can only suppose that they had never seen a man die of apoplexy; and Dr. Cabanes is undoubtedly right when he attributes it to heart-defeat after a long period of high blood-pressure. Probably a certain amount of angina pectoris also entered into the picture, which is much the same thing put into other language.

But it may be that Dr. Cabanes was too materialistic in supposing that the cause of Luther's high blood-pressure was drink, in spite of Melanchthon's explicit statement that Luther was only a moderate drinker. Probably he was no worse than other Germans of the time; and it seems to be undoubtedly true that intense emotion can permanently so put up the blood-pressure that the patient ultimately dies even if only after a great many years; and surely no man ever strained his vascular system more terribly than Martin Luther.

Luther was not a nice man; but nice men do not revolutionise the world.

Henry Fielding

IN the gloomy procession of drink, gluttony, and syphilis which makes up so large a part of history—always excepting for a moment Joan of Arc, that "one white angel of war" whom the English and French burned because she did not and could not ever become mature, as I have shown in *Post Mortem*—there is at least one very great man whom one can only pity, if my ideas about him are correct, without the faintest trace of censure—the author of that "foul, coarse and abominable" book, *Tom Jones*, which has been such a nightmare to the prude and yet shows human nature better than most of the books which are welcomed in country parsonages.

On January 1st, 1753, a young servant girl named Betty Canning disappeared from a house in Aldermanbury, London, where she had been employed as a servant; she reappeared on the 29th of the month at her mother's home, starving, half-clad, and with a fine story of abduction and imprisonment. She identified an old gipsy-woman as her assailant, who, being a gipsy, old and ugly, was promptly seized and sentenced to be hanged after the light-hearted manner of the eighteenth century. Though London was divided into two camps, for and against Betty Canning, there seems to have been no talk of a vigilance committee, probably because the great heart of the people was not stirred by evening newspapers about the woes of a little servant. One of Betty's witnesses was a little servant girl named Virtue Hall, whose delightful name alone should have induced credence; and Virtue appeared before Fielding, who was then a magistrate looking into the mystery of Betty Canning, to support Betty's claims for vengeance. If the gipsy had been a man no doubt she would have been hanged promptly; but, as she was a woman, the psychology of those days could not imagine why Betty should have accused her of abduction and a certain amount of trouble was taken to test the truth of Betty's accusations. As a result the gipsy was by a miracle let off, and Betty got seven years for perjury. Nowadays it seems quite an ordinary sort of case, where a hysterical girl will perjure her immortal soul in order to attract attention to herself, whatever may be the results to others; but the real interest to us lies in the light that it casts on the sick mind of Fielding himself; for he actually believed Virtue and published a pamphlet in support of her evidence.

This done, Fielding's health began to warn him that he must take care of himself, and he set about curing the chronic gout which had long crippled him. He took an ancient remedy of Galen's, called "the Duke of Portland's remedy"—Fielding was always fond of experimenting upon himself with quack medicines—and was advised to try the waters of Bath. Meantime he had busied himself with dogging the footsteps of no less than five gangs of street-robbers; and in the midst of the turmoil there came a peremptory message from the Duke of Newcastle to attend at Newcastle House and discuss the depredations of yet more cut-throats. For months he worked hard at the pursuit, with splendid results for the peace of London, but disastrous results upon his own health, for he had become deeply jaundiced and "fallen away to a shadow." No more was to be seen that handsome Harry Fielding who had worked so hard for literature and civic peace; whose generosity and goodness to the poor, outcast, and oppressed has become proverbial; but a wasted, dropsical man of pinched face, who could hardly leave his chair, so crippled was he with the gout and so heavy with the dropsy. The time had long gone by for Bath, if indeed it had ever existed. The winter of 1753-4 was terribly severe and his doctors told him that he must seek a warmer climate. Even Bishop Berkeley's tar-water had failed, so things must have looked black indeed for Fielding as he was carried laboriously on board the ship *Queen of Portugal* for the long voyage to Lisbon. His wife, the successor of that beloved woman whom he has immortalised in *Sophia Western* and *Amelia Booth*, accompanied him to nurse him, though I am afraid the poor lady was not much use as a nurse to a sick man whose every movement caused him pain; the very winds fought against him, and it was weeks before the ship could get away from the Isle of Wight into blue water.

It must have been a miserable voyage for Fielding; he was confined to the cabin because he could not mount the companion ladder owing to his weakness and pain. Twice he had to be tapped for his dropsy; the food was bad, his wife confined to her bed with a terrible toothache that could not be relieved because the tooth seems to have had a peculiar root that defied all attempts at removal; but he himself, sitting propped up in the stuffy cabin, wrote the most delightful and uncomplaining journal imaginable, which is quite as brilliant as, and even more moving than, any of his novels. It is written in Fielding's own half-jocular, half-satirical and wholly sympathetic style, but is entirely free from that occasional coarseness that has shocked even a generation that seems to revel in the sex-neurotic and introspective psychoanalytical novel. Better to use an occasional naughty word than to give the impression of being constantly possessed by unclean thoughts of sex, which seems to be the unhappy fate of some modern novelists.

Although he has given us an excellent description of his symptoms it is difficult to reduce it to terms of modern pathology and to name his actual sickness. I thought at first that he must have had cirrhosis of the liver, because it is well known to cause severe dropsy, wasting, haggard face, and despair. But after carefully reconsidering the symptoms I came to the conclusion that such an idea was untenable, for cirrhosis is not noted for its jaundice, and moreover it is caused by long and continuous drinking, whereas Fielding is known to have been a reasonably abstemious drinker. But there is an even more terrible disease which would even better than cirrhosis exactly suit the conditions of our problem, cancer. If we imagine Fielding to have suffered from a certain form of internal malignant tumour spreading to the peritoneum, all his symptoms would be at once explained, deep jaundice, dropsy, wasting and frightful appearance. I am assuming that Fielding's form of "dropsy" was what we now call "ascites," that is to say, an outpouring of serous fluid into the peritoneum. His so-called asthma may possibly have been due to heart trouble owing to the strain on his heart caused by oppression from the dropsy, and his "gout" to septic disease of his teeth, which would account for the toothless condition which so disfigured him towards the end of his life and prevented him from eating the ship's food.

Unlike some writers who, being possessed by their own unconscious minds, are led into filth, Fielding, though occasionally coarse, is never dirty. I remember during some months, when all the cats, dogs and roosters in the neighbourhood combined in an assault upon sleep, and an occasional kookooburra joined in the noise, I read through the whole of *Amelia* and thought it one of the most delightful books in the world; and a rereading of it tends to confirm me in that belief. Amelia, for all her scarred nose, is one of the most charming women in fiction, though she had a great deal to put up with in her husband,

Captain Booth, and though she *would* call him "Billy."

Fielding himself was what the Americans would call a "he-man." He was not one of the miserable, whining, introspective heroes of post-war fiction; and in Tom Jones and Captain Booth he has drawn a man as he thought a man should be, and as good men probably are if we would stop our ears to the howls of the old women. And these heroes of his were probably drawn from himself. That terrible ironic creature, Jonathan Wild, of course represents his knowledge of the Old Bailey; it is a grim book, and far too ironical for most people, though it has not the sardonic and shuddering laughter of Dean Swift and his Struldbrugs.

But if he had cancer when he started on his last voyage he must have had it coming on when he believed Virtue's tarradiddle, and possibly it was because of his poor health that he believed her. No man with a cancer beginning to gnaw at his vitals could possibly take the trouble to cross-examine a brazen hussy who was determined to deceive him, and we can even understand that chapter in *Amelia* when he stops the narrative to deliver a violent attack upon the medical profession, possibly because when he was writing *Amelia* he must occasionally have felt the slight twinge and noticed the slight jaundice that would be the first symptom that all was not well.

But he was a very kind man, even as a magistrate. He knew too much about human nature to be harsh with anybody, and possibly Virtue, in telling untruths, had touched a soft spot in his generous heart; in other words, Virtue and Betty must have "vamped" him.

King James I

IT would be easier to say what was not the matter with this walking pathological museum than to name his actual disease. From early youth till death his life was one long pain. He could hardly walk until he was nearly six years old, and this defect was attributed by his physician, Sir Theodore Mayerne, to the bad milk of a drunken wet-nurse. Mayerne,[10] who left a full account of James's health, seems to have been an acute man, but nowadays we should rather attribute the somewhat neurotic troubles from which James suffered to his unconscious infantile disgust at the drunken woman than to the influence of her bad milk.

He himself certainly did not use milk as his drink when he came to years of "discretion." He was afflicted with the normal gigantic appetite of kings in those days. He ate anything and everything so long as it could be eaten: not even Charles V could have excelled his prowess. He drank, indiscriminately, beer, spirits, Spanish

[10] *British Medical Journal,* 1910.

wines, cider, sweet French wines, and muscatel, probably mixing them all right royally. His interior organs were always too full, and he got rid of the vast surplus in whatever disgusting way, up or down, happened to be convenient, so, in every way, he must have been a most unpleasant companion.

He was subject to catarrh, and was much affected by cold and damp; he was constantly spitting, hawking, and blowing his nose. As handkerchiefs were not then in general use, I have heard that he used his sleeve or his finger and thumb, which would not add to his "clubability." He had some difficulty in swallowing, owing, as Sir Theodore puts it, to some narrowing of his fauces, inherited from his mother, Mary Queen of Scots, and from his grandfather, James V of Scotland. Putting two and two together, the constant blowing of his nose and the "narrowing" of his throat, one imagines that probably the poor man suffered from adenoids and enlarged tonsils. He occasionally suffered from gravel, often accompanied by blood. He constantly suffered from another ignoble trouble, which in the course of years bled copiously. If he was specially worried in mind or body—and a king is always worried— he would become jaundiced. Whenever anything more than usually alarming occurred, the unhappy man would get diarrhœa, just like an anxious student awaiting his interview with the examiners. He used faithfully to insist on his being bled every day, until his least dignified ailment saved the doctors the trouble. When he dismissed his Parliament of 1610 apparently his diarrhœa became profuse. In fact, if you can think of any ailment that I have not mentioned from which he suffered—so be it that it was excessively undignified—I wish you would tell me what it was.

He had a truly psychasthenic dread of pain, yet hated all doctors, possibly because he had suffered too much at our hands. His teeth were all decayed, so that he could chew nothing, but had perforce to bolt his food. A man with the decayed teeth that so distinguished the "most learned fool in Christendom" would naturally in time suffer from arthritis; and in middle age this complaint so crippled him that he could hardly mount his horse. He detested purgatives, and considered that any medicine, to do good, must act upon the bowels without griping the patient; till late in his life he would not even allow an enema, probably because it hurt him.

With death came, as usual, a little of that dignity that was so sadly lacking in his life. S.

R. Gardiner says that he died of a fever, but it is impossible even to guess at its nature. Early, in the morning of March 27th, 1625, he was so ill that he had to send for his son Prince Charles, who came running into the king's room in a night-shirt. Seeing his son, King James tried to raise himself on his pillows and to say something; but his voice had become so weak as to be inaudible, so that even then he failed. He was understood to say "Veni, Domine Jesu," and soon his breathing ceased; in fact, like most people, he passed painlessly into the sleep that knows no waking. He had done with all his pain and constant discomfort, and, so far as he knew, with the misunderstanding that afflicted him in his life in England and has certainly afflicted his memory ever since. Poor James did not have a chance from his infancy. It has been said that he failed because he did not understand the English people; but how could you expect him to do that when he was constantly worried by the most distressing and undignified of all ailments? And was it not also equally their duty to try to understand him?

They held a post-mortem examination upon him, because there were the usual accusations of poisoning, apparently founded largely upon the swelling of his tongue. They found that his heart was enormously enlarged, and that in his left kidney, which was greatly shrunken, there reposed two stones, from which doubtless had come that gravel which had so afflicted him during his life. Possibly his enlarged heart and swollen tongue, together with his vast overeating and drinking, may have meant that King James I had chronic Bright's disease.

How far the drunken wet-nurse may have influenced his later life no one can say; but it is quite possible that the unconscious infant may have felt a disgust that went far to cause that nervousness and lack of dignity of which his subjects complained. But how could any man be dignified when he was suffering constantly from gravel and the other tormenting, itching, weakening, and ignoble trouble?

But surely we have omitted the most important point in James's supposed character: the unnatural offences of which he was suspected. Well, Sir Theodore Mayerne, who has told us so frankly all about his hawking and spitting, his diarrhœa, his gravel, his stones, and his bleeding hæmorrhoids, does not seem to know anything about the unnatural offences. The pure mind always seems to turn towards this sort of offence when it thinks of its neighbour. In 1642, according to the

American Mercury of April, 1924, the Puritans, hardly settled down in the American colonies, were already accusing each other of the most awful sexual offences. And before convicting James of such offences one would prefer the evidence of a level-headed doctor to that of all the seventeenth-century Puritans in the world.

It is strange how minds, under the influence of fierce religious fervour, always turn, and always have turned, to unnatural sexual offences. It is not a product of patristic Christianity, as so many have thought. On reading *The Golden Ass*, of Apuleius, one must be struck with the amazing moral filth of the Roman Empire. After wading through hundreds of pages of gay and libidinous dirt, one suddenly finds that one is assisting in religious propaganda. Apuleius paints his fellow-countrymen and women in such black colours simply because he wants them to join in the worship of the Great Mother, which was then so formidable a rival to Christianity in the Roman Empire.

So, considering the known facts of religious propaganda, I do not believe a single word of the slanders upon James I. There were Puritans about.

It is possible that Petronius, in his *Satyricon*—

if he wrote it—drew a truthful picture of the Empire under Nero, because he does not profess to moralise or to convert anybody whatever to any supposed better religion. One is sometimes inclined to agree with Gibbon that "all (*organised*) religions are equally false and equally useful."

But it would be absurd to suppose that James the Sixth and First was merely the ridiculous creature that I have depicted here. Those who wish to prove that he was a coward have first to account for the known fact that, until his knees stiffened under the influence of his decayed teeth, he was a brave and first-class horseman. It may be true that he could never bear the sight of a drawn sword; neither could Lord Roberts bear the sight of a cat. Before he was dragged to England he did for Scotland what the heavy-handed Tudors did for South Britain. By his skill and diplomacy he welded even fierce little Scotland into an orderly country, and taught the Scots lords and the ministers of the General Assembly that the king was their master.

King Charles I

DOCTORS seldom take much interest in politics. It is their general experience that for all the tumult and the shoutings of politicians nobody ever seems one penny the better for the uproar, for vast sums are wasted which would be much better expended in a way that we really do know something about, such as the cure of disease and the public health generally. In some ways the most interesting thing about the "Martyred Monarch" is the expression of wistful melancholy which is shown on the famous portrait by Van Dyck. It is undoubtedly due to this portrait that so much sympathy has always been felt for him; and the tragedy of King Charles has always impressed thoughtful men as a tragedy from the Greek.

In his early youth he stammered so badly that until he was ten he could hardly speak at all. Stammering is supposed to be a nervous habit due to a psychasthenic phobia; and the worst case of stammering that I ever knew was said to have been acquired by a nervous child of three, owing

143

to a negligent nurse having locked him up in a dark cupboard while she read novels. Stammerers often express themselves by their pen; and several eminent writers, both in the past and in the present day, have been stammerers. Not less acute than other men—indeed often far more acute than the average—yet as they are invariably shy they are incapable of showing it in conversation; and the brutal outburst of Carlyle concerning poor Charles Lamb reflects an opinion that is too often held by the impatient and intolerant.

King Charles had during his day the finest collection of art-treasures in Europe; and in that fact we see the essentially refined and artistic character of the man, for he not only had the treasures, but understood them. Stammering often tends to improve as the man grows older. Demosthenes is said to have cured himself by shouting at the sea waves, while King Charles succeeded to a large extent by speaking with extraordinary slowness and dignity, though to some extent the habit remained with him to the end. Strangely enough the sad and pathetic expression on Van Dyck's portrait is not unlike the sad and pathetic expression on the famous portrait statue of Demosthenes by Polyeuctes; although of course

Demosthenes was of a much more aggressive character and more ready to make himself felt in public than Charles Stuart.

But in Van Dyck's portrait we see probably the unconscious infantile fear in the baby Charles that ultimately led him to stammer; and possibly in the utterly wrong-headed obstinacy of the king in holding on to an impossible position, we see the determination that resulted in his curing himself sufficiently to attain the crown.

An incident occurred during his trial that may have led to a false impression. "They will not suffer me to speak," he cried brokenly as they led him away. Is it possible that during that dreadful moment the old bad habit of his childish days returned, so that King Charles actually *could* not speak for the time?

He is said to have been one of the few kings of really noble domestic character, a faithful husband and affectionate father. Yet though he could be faithful to his wife he could not help telling lies to his friends.

> "Vanquished in life his death
>   By beauty made amends;
>   The passing of his breath
>   Won its defeated ends."

Charles was temperate, chaste and serious; he treated those about him with punctilious courtesy and expected the same in return.

But it may be that in the twistings and turnings of his political career we see the qualities that are not inconsistent with the artistic temperament.

As for the apparent cause of Charles's stammering, that is quite impossible even to guess. It is possible that he, a naturally sensitive and refined little boy, may have been unconsciously terrified by his father's unpleasant personal habits. At any rate, let us keep a soft spot in our hearts for the ill-fated king.

Whence came the somewhat nervous strain that runs, like a brass thread, through the whole dynasty of the Stuarts, I hesitate to speculate: perhaps from Darnley, father of James I. They always make me think of a set of naughty children wedged between the great gloomy Tudors and the unpleasant Hanoverians. There was James I, who is generally held by the English to have been an egregious person; next, Charles I, who, probably, would have done better as a poet; then Charles II, who was by far the cleverest of them, but was too lazy; and lastly the gloomy and exceedingly immoral—if all tales are true—James

146

II, who was a man too much under the influence
of religion. It is said that he used to get absolution after every time that he visited his mistress.
Then there was that poor, lonely, stupid Anne,
who could not, for some reason, rear a single one
of her numerous children.

King Charles II

A S the best thing that we hear of the life of
King Charles II is the manner of his leav-
ing it, I confine myself to a description of his
death. You will get a moderately good account
of it in Bishop Burnet's history, of which Swift
was so scornful; and a recognisable account of
it in Lord Macaulay, written with all the fixed
ideas of the early nineteenth century colouring the
ink; but the real truth appeared in an article in
the *British Medical Journal* for 1910, which again
was drawn largely from Dr. Raymond Crawfurd's
Last Days of Charles II. As Dr. Crawfurd gives
the official report of Sir Charles Scarburgh, one
of the consultants in attendance at the time, probably we may take it that we have the exact details
so far as the medical science of 1685 could give
them.

Towards the end of 1684 the king did not
feel quite well: he was irritable and depressed,
and thought it wise to remain indoors during the
mornings, instead of taking his usual active walks.

He attributed his illness to gout. It would be interesting to speculate on what the disease actually was that so often was called "gout" in the sixteenth and seventeenth centuries. There are many conditions which cause symptoms such as might be mistaken for gout; let us leave it at that, for even to-day a doctor, forced to give to a vague complaint a name, sometimes takes refuge in the euphemism "rheumatic gout." During these few days indoors he amused himself by playing with mercury in his laboratory, for, as is well known, he was of scientific bent. At last came the fateful morning, Monday, February 2nd, 1685. At eight o'clock the king, while being shaved, fell back with a cry into the arms of an attendant, Lord Aylesbury. According to Dr. Scarburgh, "Charles, having just left his bed, was walking about quietly in his bedchamber when he felt some unusual disturbance in his brain, which was followed by loss of speech and violent convulsions." There happened to be present at the time two of the king's physicians who, so as promptly to forestall so serious a danger to "this best of kings," as Scarburgh has it, opened a vein in his right arm and drew 16 ounces of blood. As a matter of fact, this assault, though seemingly homicidal, was probably as good a thing as could have been done for him, though few doctors would have the moral courage to do it to-day. His head was closely shaved; his neck and shoulders were blistered and scarified; emetics, purgatives and clysters were administered, and every reputable doctor, regardless of his religion, was summoned to the defence. Whitehall must have presented a lively spectacle that winter morning with all the periwigs and silver buckles and gold-headed canes and wise faces. In fact, they did what they could: if they had known that the cause of the convulsions was probably that the king's kidneys had "gone on strike," they could have done little more than endeavour to get rid of the poisons that must have been circulating in his body by some other effluent than by the urine. After about two hours their efforts were crowned with success. The king, whose face had been hideously black,—i.e., cyanosed—and whose eyes had been rolling this way and that, woke up, and proceeded to give an account of himself. The poisons had for a time been got out of his body; but only for a time. He said that, not feeling very well when he awakened, he had gone to his private closet to get some "king's drops," which Dr. Crawfurd explains to have been "a volatile extract of bone made in the king's laboratory according to the formula of the late Dr. Goddard, and in high repute on the Continent."

Charles was then out of immediate danger, and during the Tuesday he remained fairly well except for some soreness about the neck and mouth, which was probably due to the efforts that had had to be made to get him to swallow his medicines. Just so to-day, a patient occasionally wakes up from an anæsthetic with a stiff jaw after the efforts which have had to be made to pull his tongue forward if his breathing has given trouble while he was unconscious. Charles complained of great pain in his interior, which was probably less a symptom of his illness than of the violent purgatives that had been forced down his throat; but to the horrified Bishop Burnet it was "agonies."

The doctors, pestered by the ministers of the Crown to give the king's illness a name, were greatly perturbed, and all fourteen [11] of them entered into many grave consultations one with another. On the afternoon of Wednesday, February 4th, the convulsions returned, and as intermittent fever was then especially prevalent in and about London they said that probably His Majesty was suffering from that complaint, though

[11] Some say sixteen.

to be sure the violent convulsions, cyanosed skin, loss of speech, and turning of the eyeballs did not look quite like intermittent fever. But the council was satisfied, which, to the doctors wrestling with a mysterious and complex disease, was probably all that they could expect, for it enabled them to say that they now knew what to do, and that, apparently, the king was in no great immediate danger. As the *British Medical Journal* rather unkindly points out: "On June 21st, 1902, the late King Edward's Private Secretary wrote that there was not a word of truth in the rumours that had been floating about concerning His Majesty's health, though on June 24th the coronation was postponed and he had to be operated on for appendicitis"; though, considering what a sudden thing acute appendicitis is, there is little wonder that three days before anyone might not have known of his coming ill health.

On the Thursday occurred those dramatic events of which conventional historians have made so much. When he was first taken ill on the Monday his poor wife had hurried to his side, and had taken the place of at least one of his mistresses in nursing him. Catherine of Braganza may not have had sufficient physical charm to keep his wayward fancy, and may not have been able to bear

And the tongue? Quite frequently the tongue and larynx suddenly swell up in chronic Bright's disease, and the patient suffocates before he can obtain relief. King Charles was indeed poisoned, though not by human agency. He was poisoned by the toxins which should have been excreted by his own kidneys, but could not be got rid of by any human aid; that is to say, he probably died of uræmia from chronic Bright's disease.

A post-mortem examination was held, so we can get even further evidence. One could not expect a doctor in the seventeenth century to observe that his kidneys were obviously diseased, or that part of his brain was œdematous or softened, as often happens in Bright's disease, and would no doubt cause the loss of speech. But they did observe that his heart was enlarged, a most significant point.

I remember one of the very first private patients that I ever had, nearly thirty years ago. A middle-aged Englishman had come to Sydney from China for his health, apparently feeling fairly well, though debilitated by the tropical climate. Suddenly, as he was shaving, he was taken ill with a violent fit of convulsions, and, in spite of all that we could do for him, died in the course of two or three days with symptoms that exactly resembled those so graphically portrayed by Lord Macaulay and Dr. Crawfurd.

There is much of extraordinary interest to be found in Dr. Crawfurd's book which gives the fantastic truth about medicine in 1685,[13] I can only advise you to read the book. In spite of the queer medicines that they used to prescribe I fancy that doctors at that time had more common sense than we moderns seem to think, and I very much doubt if anything could have saved King Charles's life, except perhaps for a short time. He had come to his end. Our treatment would have been less drastic, but little more successful.

The cause of chronic Bright's disease is not definitely known. It has been attributed to innumerable things; indeed, to everything which any given physician does not like himself; and comparatively recently it has even been attributed to improper feeding in infancy, so far back in life are its roots supposed to go. Indeed, it is generally thought to be hereditary; but probably it is still a mystery, though overeating and overdrinking may have something to do with it, not to mention, of course, syphilis, but so many men who have not had syphilis die of chronic Bright's

[13] Macaulay makes such fun of the poor doctors, with many sensational adjectives, but I shall not reprint it here.

disease that it would not be fair to state it as the cause.

But why is it that Henri Quatre, whose morals were little if at all better than those of Charles, has become a national hero, while Charles is always held up as a byword for infamy? I do not know; but the usual explanation is that the English are at heart Puritans, and M. Chevrillon, in his recent essays on English literature, has accepted that as the reason for the popularity of Kipling and Galsworthy. But I sometimes wonder whether, had England been more successful under Charles II, so much would have been heard of his immorality. After all, Lord Nelson was not a Joseph, but he saved England from Napoleon; whereas Charles II saw the Dutch fleet in the Thames, and ran about chasing butterflies while the guns thundered.

All medical students, and most doctors, pass through a period when they are convinced that they have chronic Bright's disease, and it is not till after visiting their physicians in an agony of mind that they are relieved of their mental distress. Let not a lay reader be silly enough to copy these apprehensive doctors. No man can be his own physician.

But perhaps the most interesting things about

Charles II are the sterility of his wife, Catherine of Braganza, and his affection for "poor Nelly," which she undoubtedly returned. Catherine appears to have been a convent-bred maiden with beautiful eyes. She was by no means the king's first or last love; and several months after the marriage she fell ill of some sickness that brought her to death's door, so that they had to administer extreme unction. It was probably owing to this illness that she never had a child, and was afterwards often ill. Such a trouble as pelvic peritonitis, with inflammation of the Fallopian tubes, often causes sterility. It is Nature's stupid way of saving the patient's life that she isolates the inflammation and seals the tubes, so that the woman indeed lives, but miserable, sterile, neurasthenic, and in constant pain. What was the actual cause of the illness in Catherine's case it is impossible to say. One ventures to hazard a guess that the real cause of Catherine's sterility was simply adhesions and blocked Fallopian tubes; it is certain that it had nothing to do with King Charles's potency, because he had many natural children by other women. It is in that severe illness several months after she was married that the explanation of her sterility probably lies. We see innumerable cases of this sort to-day.

About Nell Gwynn. She was herself the daughter of a prostitute who, in a fit of drink, one night fell into a ditch and was drowned. Her charm over the king probably lay in her wit and recklessness; she dared to say to him things that no one else on earth ventured. She was faithful to him after he had won her—if indeed she took much winning. Other women, such as La Belle Stuart, and Louise de Querouaille, pretended to resist him for a time, but Nell seems to have been really fond of him and did not resist at all. Remember she was, before she became an actress, an orange-girl—that is to say, a prostitute. Everything we hear of her tells of her uniform kindness and generosity; she was of course extremely loose in her conduct and morals, but she seems to have cared little for money. She died about two years after the king, apparently of a stroke that had brought on one-sided paralysis or hemiplegia; and considering the assured facts of her youth, and the early age at which she died, that stroke was probably caused by syphilis, which had lain latent in her ever since the time when she sold herself with her oranges in the pit of Drury Lane.

But no person should attempt to describe the life either of Charles II or Nell Gwynn who has the slightest tendency to moralise; for neither the wittiest of the Stuarts nor the clever little actress can be explained on conventional codes of morality. It is the attempt to consider Charles II as if he had been a child of Queen Victoria, and to moralise over him, that makes most books about him so repulsive.

But Nell did not try to enter politics; she resisted the temptation to be queen, even if the opportunity had ever offered. She knew that her only function in life was to charm; and with the coldly realistic outlook on life that is common to all prostitutes, she knew that in the position of a queen she must come up against the harsh facts of reality, and that, like Anne Boleyn, she would probably lose her head in every sense of the word. Mere power to charm is not for a queen. Nell's memory, owing to her wisdom and self-restraint, has been tenderly treated by the English people, in spite of that prudery which has scoffed at the real cleverness of her royal lover. Nell Gwynn, to use her own coarse words, was content to remain "the Protestant whore," the cleverness of her tongue enabled her to keep her place at Court against all rivals, and her charm even impresses us to-day, who have never seen her dance nor heard her cockney witticisms. "Let not poor Nelly" fade from our memories.

Henri Quatre

THE great thing about Henri Quatre, from the point of view of a medical essayist, is that no person of an anti-syphilitic fury will expect him to be classed as an awful warning of the devastations of that disease. Poor Henri died of good honest assassination, the product of an even worse disease than syphilis—sectarian intolerance. A disease which could cause the awful wars of Henri's own life, and a few years later the most dreadful of all wars—the Thirty Years' —need not fear to be classed alongside even the most disreputable and destructive of human disorders. And the fact that nobody in these terrible wars ever had the least idea why people were killing each other only makes the marvel of sectarian intolerance even more amazing than it is. Of course, there is no such thing as *religious* intolerance. Religion should make war impossible, and should inculcate tolerance for other people's opinions. Did the good-natured and kindly gods of old Greece ever breed a religious war? Did anybody ever go swashbuckling in helmet and armour

163

for Zeus or Aphrodite? Unless perhaps Aphrodite to him meant some individual woman who had been raped from her home, such as Helen of Troy; and Helen probably meant some vague abstraction of a Greek woman as opposed to a barbarian, if she did not symbolise Greek trade through the Hellespont, obstructed by Trojan robber bands. The Marxian materialist view of history grows rather attractive when it is applied to people who have been dead three thousand years.

Quite apart from the murderous sectarian squabbles, which have been dignified by the name of religious wars, the life of Henri Quatre, very properly classed as one of the heroes of France, is extraordinarily interesting to a doctor. But in many ways the most interesting thing about him was his relations with women. Henri may have had some conscience about religion—though I doubt it—but, like our own Charles II, he had absolutely no conscience about women. To him, whether he was married or not, any pretty girl was fair game; and those who care to read pornography can find plenty of it in the record of his life. The seventeenth century was a period of bitter sectarian differences, and it was a time when the divine right of kings to possess pretty girls was elevated almost to an article of faith. Thus we had the marvellous spectacles of King Henri IV and King Charles II, of whom the one became a national hero, the other a byword for flippancy and falsehood. I am not going to be led into any temptation to find the cause of the one phenomenon in the other—to say that if it had not been a period of such bitter sectarianism the virtue of girls might have been more sacred to kings, because there have been good kings and bad kings at all times; girls have been virtuous or wanton, whatever their religion; and the seventeenth century was not the only century in history. The sixteenth and eighteenth could show instances of moral depravity quite as bad as that of either Henri Quatre or Charles Stuart. Let us see what a doctor may be able to say about Henri Quatre.

When he was about nineteen he married Marguerite de Valois, the third of that name, who has achieved fame under the popular name of Reine Margot. She was sister to King Henri III of France; our Henri was at that time only king of Navarre; his little kingdom lay in the south of France, near the borders of Spain. His father had been Anthony of Bourbon; his mother Joan of Albret. Joan had agreed to the marriage with a

very heavy heart: she feared the bright eyes of the
Catholic enchantress who was to bewitch her own
beloved son. She herself was a Huguenot, who
looked upon Marguerite as sent directly from the
devil. If Marguerite had really been sent by
Satan to the inferno of Parisian wickedness she
needed no great ensnaring; for, when she married
the good Henri of Navarre, simple young country
bumpkin that he was, she is said to have already
had an affair with the Duke of Guise, and her
reputation for virtue would not have passed any
great test. She was pretty, and what was more
potent, she had a peculiar charm of manner that
enabled her to capture all but the most resistant
of men. Many of us remember how Marguerite,
in the "Huguenots" of Meyerbeer, dances along
the stage singing to her lute and plangent orches-
tral pizzicati "The fair land of Touraine." Although this, according to Wagner, is very in-
artistic, still, it is very charming, and has no doubt
left Marguerite for us moderns with a character
that is more beautiful than it really was. She
could no more resist enchanting a man than Henri
could resist trying to possess a good-looking girl:
the bonds of matrimony sat very lightly upon
both. There was no love in the marriage, which
was, almost more cynically than most royal mar-

riages, simply an affair of State. Catherine de Medici, Marguerite's mother, wished to convert Henri to the Catholic faith, and at the same time to make him an enemy of Spain, which, under Don John of Austria, had just won the earth-shaking victory of Lepanto.

But Marguerite could do something else besides make love: she could write. At a time when every one else was striving to be distinguished in style Marguerite wrote as simply and clearly as if she were speaking; and her *Memories* are therefore still delightful to read. Just after her marriage the massacre of St. Bartholomew broke out. Let the royal lady tell how it affected herself. "An hour later, while I was fast asleep, someone came beating at my door with hands and feet, and shouting Navarre, Navarre! My nurse, thinking it was my husband, ran to open the door. It was a gentleman, wounded by a sword-thrust in the elbow, and his arm cut by a halberd, who rushed into my room pursued by four archers. Seeking safety he threw himself on my bed. Feeling this man clutching me I threw myself into the open space between the bed and the wall, where, he still grasping me, we both rolled over, both screaming and both equally frightened. Fortunately the Captain of my Guards, M. de Nancay, came by, and seeing me in such a plight could not help laughing, but drove the archers out of the room, and gave me the life of the poor gentleman, who was still clinging to me, and whom I caused to be tended in my dressing-room till he was quite cured. While I changed my night-dress,"—Marguerite was lucky to be wearing one in 1572—"for he had covered me with his blood, M. de Nancay told me what had happened, and assured me that my husband was in the king's room and was quite safe. Making me throw on a dressing-gown, he led me to the room of my sister, Madame de Lorraine, which I reached more dead than alive; just as I was going into the anteroom a gentleman, trying to escape from the archers who were pursuing him, fell dead three paces from me. I too fell half-fainting into the arms of M. de Nancay, and felt as if the same blow had pierced us both."

Dumas describes this incident in *Marguerite de Valois;* but his description is no more vivid than Marguerite's. The temptation to make the poor fugitive the hero of his book was too great, and he turned the ill-fated De la Mole into Marguerite's unwilling bedfellow on that night of weeping. I dare say that Marguerite was not sorry to be able to save the poor man's life, even though Dumas makes her behave far from generously to his hero later. If I remember rightly she has him tortured by the "boot."

Queen Joan, her mother-in-law, describes her as being very pretty, but one could not see her face for the paint; she was rather too stout, and was tightly laced. Afterwards, when she had abandoned all sense of decency, she became enormously fat, and could hardly get through an ordinary door. Her intelligence and great fondness for reading probably did not make Henri love her any better, because he could never finish a serious book. She said about her brother Henri III that if all the treachery in the world should perish Henri III had enough to restock it; so it is clear that brother and sister did not really love one another; and probably Marguerite could not resist the temptation to make a scathing epigram.

But Joan need not have been so perturbed over her son falling into the hands of the satanic Marguerite, for, if all tales were true, she was no great saint herself. Once, when Henri III was in a particularly bad temper, he went to Marguerite in church and called her all manner of abominable names, so that she turned and ran weeping out of the church. Later he went up to

Henri Quatre and half-apologised for his rude-
ness, explaining it because of some unfortunate
incidents that had been rumoured about Queen
Joan's own virtue. Henri laughed, and afterwards said, "What a nice fellow he must be! He
thinks by saying that I am a bastard to make up
for calling my wife a prostitute!" That was
really much the sort of thing that our own beloved Charles II might have said; and it shows
Henri Quatre as a maker of epigrams with just
sufficient truth in them to hurt. And all done
with a kindly smile, too.

When the civil war broke out Henri of Navarre took the lead with furious energy on the
Protestant side; and it was then that he won
his reputation for soldiering and for romance.
The white plume of Navarre has been an ori-
flamme for many a novelist ever since. And it
was more than romance, though treated roman-
tically by Macaulay in his *Battle of Ivry*.
Henry had bound upon his head a great plume
of white peacock feathers just before the battle.
"Should the standards fall," he cried, "rally round
the white plume of Navarre. I promise you that
it shall be found in the thickest of the fighting."
He made good his boast, for he charged the Catholics two horses' lengths ahead of his followers,

and fought furiously until his sword was beaten out of shape and his right arm swelled with over-exertion—I suppose the lymphatics of the arm became somehow obstructed, but I confess I do not quite understand the pathological condition; still, the incident made a great impression upon his soldiers and gave Henri of Navarre a name for immense courage and enterprise. As a result of many hours' fierce fighting the Protestants swept the field, partly because the Swiss merce-naries, finding that the League had not paid their wages, surrendered incontinently. "Pas d'argent —pas de Suisse," was their excellent motto, which the League should have remembered. If Henri had swept on to Paris the opinion is that he might have entered it with very little trouble. But he had no money, he had fired away all his ammunition, and the roads were made impassable by recent rains; moreover, even if Paris had opened her gates to him the Pope would never have ceased his hostility to a Protestant king of France; and once more the old spectre of civil war, interminable, bloodthirsty, and dreadful, would have arisen. And, after all, the majority of Frenchmen were Catholic; and the mighty power of Spain waited just over the Pyrenees to help the Pope if indeterminate civil war should

occur. Paris lay, weakly defended, ready for
assault; but it would have been a terrible crime
for Henri to give the word, and to subject his
capital to a worse than St. Bartholomew. So he
agreed to "receive instruction," saying before he
did so that his religion was that of all brave men.
Paris, strictly invested, suffered the worst horrors
of famine. Soldiers killed and ate stray children,
and a woman even salted down and ate her own
babies who had died of starvation. It is said
that the poor creature went "melancholy" from
this Thyestian feast, and who can wonder? The
great Alexander Farnese, Prince of Parma, was
arriving from the Netherlands with a relieving
army of Spaniards; he outmanœuvred Henri, and
opened navigation to the beleaguered city. Henri
could neither pay his men nor would he permit
them to pay themselves by the sack of the city,
so naturally they went home. Henri and a few
faithful friends and horse soldiers retired to watch
and hope. Thus was fulfilled the prophecy of
his great, though somewhat thrifty, ally, Elizabeth of England, that "if God shall, by His
merciful grace, grant you victory, I swear to you
that it will be more than your carelessness de-
serves." Kipling, in an unforgettable phrase, has
told us all about the "female of the species";

and in many ways, Elizabeth was the female of the species to which Henri Quatre belonged. The daughter of Henry VIII would have had no mercy if her own ends had been at stake. And yet, I don't know. Tilly a few years afterwards showed at Magdeburg the horrors that could be perpetrated by religious enthusiasts; and one hates to think that Elizabeth's famous patriotism could ever have allowed her to sacrifice London for a point of belief. Henri Quatre had not only allowed friends in Paris to be fed while he was supposed to be investing it savagely, but he had allowed it to slip through his fingers when he might have captured it, all through a tender-heartedness that would spare its citizens the horrors of a Magdeburgian sack. It is no wonder that with all his faults he is one of the heroes of France. Then Parma, finding that the Parisians hated Spanish pride more than they hated French Protestants, went away with his invincible army; and as soon as his back was turned Henri resumed the siege. Parma had proved, if nothing more, that he was a better strategist than Henri Quatre; but Paris returned to the old misery of starvation and disease, a misery that it has so often braved nobly.

And now began Henri's more serious troubles

with women. For a long time he had an affair with one Madame de Grasmont, whom he called Corisande. To her he wrote the most passionate of letters. Anybody would think to read them that he really loved her; but even as he besieged Paris he had fallen in love with the abbesses of Poissy and Montmartre, whose profession should have taught them wisdom if not virtue. Now came a more serious affair. In 1590 he met a Gabrielle d'Estrees, with whom he fell violently in love while he was "carrying on" with the other three ladies. She already had a beautiful lover; but that did not matter to Henri Quatre. Probably it only caused him to admire her the more. He slipped through detachments of the enemy dressed as a woodcutter with a bundle of straw on his head to visit her: a nice romantic and undignified action for a king; but we shall see later, as he grew older, how he could stoop even lower. For the present the problem was how to gain possession of Gabrielle, get rid of Corisande, and set up a nominal possessor who should not be a rival in Gabrielle's heart. He got her father to marry Gabrielle to a M. de Liancourt, an aged widower with eleven children, while Henri IV enjoyed the *droits de seigneur*. Corisande, growing old, dropped out of the picture.

Then came a fierce struggle for Rouen, with Parma hovering ready to give battle. Again he showed his superiority to Henri Quatre as a strategist by transporting his army secretly across the Seine and escaping Henri's threatened attack. Henri had a much larger army than Parma's, and it was only Parma's extraordinary skill that saved him from destruction. But now came the end of the long war; for Parma died and Henri turned Catholic. "Paris is well worth a Mass!" as he did not say. We have always been taught to consider this as an act of shameless cynicism; but there was a great deal to be said in Henri's favour: certainly from the point of view of the twentieth century his action was the only thing that could have brought peace to his country. Though Parma was dead, Spain was still powerful and vengeful; the Catholic priests called Henri heretic, relapsed miscreant, devil and bastard, whom the soldiers knew to be a kind and generous friend, always smiling and ready to help. Gabrielle—"charmante Gabrielle," who has given her name to a song that Henri wrote in her honour —urged him to turn Catholic, that the Pope might perhaps divorce Marguerite and let him marry Gabrielle. So Henri yielded, threw his scruples to the winds, and embraced the Old Religion;

though his embrace was probably not so ardent as those which he gave to the abbesses, who more corporeally represented the faith to which he yielded.

An amusing sidelight on his character is thrown by his message to Queen Elizabeth by the mouth of her supposed lover Essex, whom she had been rating soundly because he had lost too many Englishmen in Henri's wars. The irate Virgin was so flattered by Henri's praise of her beauty and charm that it needed all her caution and frugality to keep England from plunging single-handed into yet another great war with Spain on his behalf. Happily for us she had sense enough to keep out of it; and before her help became necessary Henri had gone to Mass. When Henri fell so shamelessly in love with Gabrielle he was thirty-five years of age, and perhaps the ordinary neurasthenia of middle age began to trouble him—that cause of so much marital unhappiness and so many divorces. But, if any one woman could be said to have captured his heart, it was undoubtedly Gabrielle. I once read an account of her written by a lady, possibly unmarried. Anyhow, none would have guessed from this extremely proper description that she was Henri's official mistress; the good lady seems

never to have heard of a man being anything but
a woman's husband. Gabrielle was rather ample
of figure—Henri seems to have liked his women
fat—and had deep blue eyes and golden hair.
Her face was kind and smiling, her manner gentle;
before she fell in love with Henri her morals
had been, to say the least, unconventional; after
she admitted the king to her friendship she continued her relations with the lover who had inno-
cently introduced her to this more enterprising
king. She was extravagant, and the king loaded
her with jewels at a time when he said he was
penniless; created her Marchioness of Monceaux
and Duchess of Beaufort. He was as faithful to
her as it was possible for him to be to any woman,
which is not saying very much. At any rate his
amours were henceforth conducted with a certain
amount of decency and discretion. When she
died the only book found in her possession was her
"book of hours." Except for her easy morals
it would be impossible to find a greater contrast
than that between her and Marguerite, who could
wrap herself in learned books, play the lute, and
write like a novelist. It would seem impossible
for even "Aunt Tabitha" of a lady's newspaper
to give to Marguerite de Valois any hints on the
art of managing a husband; but it is clear that she

did not go the right way about it with Henri of Navarre; and Gabrielle d'Estrees was evidently much more to his taste, for he remained approximately, though not bigotedly, faithful to her till she died. In justice to Marguerite it is only fair to say that she never liked him; she was forced by mother and brother into marrying him; and probably even a sixteenth-century princess had her preferences. The ultimate result was that Gabrielle became a sort of idol among the people, who overlooked her unusual position for the sake of her wide-set blue eyes and kind smile; and a few years after she died she was already a legend. To this day she and Henri Quatre are greeted with a kindly smile among the French when one mentions them, and "charmante Gabrielle" is still a well-known song.

As the years rolled by she bore him several children, and more and more took the position of his wife. He became still more infatuated with her; and she, for her part, abandoned the life of dissipation which is said to have distinguished her youth. Henri wanted to marry her; she must have had great powers of fascination to make him so faithful after so many years. The idea was to procure a divorce from Marguerite and elevate his mistress to the throne. But just before the proposed marriage Gabrielle went to Paris and stayed at the house of an Italian named Zamet. On April 7th, 1599, she became very ill, and was artificially delivered of a dead child on the 9th. She fell into violent convulsions; on the 10th she became unconscious, and that evening she died. Of course Sully, who did not like her—for even Gabrielle had her enemies—hinted that she was poisoned—such was the reputation of the Italians in Paris at that time—and Sully's ill-natured hint has evidently influenced historians to this day, for the good lady whom I quoted above repeats it as at least probable. But is it not much more probable that she died of puerperal eclampsia? She was middle-aged; she had had several children; she was far from slight in figure. At the Royal Hospital for Women in Sydney we find that most of these women who die nowadays from eclampsia are very much like Gabrielle in age, figure, and the number of their children. Of course it is impossible to say definitely; but I should be very much surprised to find that Gabrielle's kidneys were absolutely healthy during that last year of her life. And it is quite possible that in that last confinement Gabrielle in this way paid the penalty for her dissipation in early youth. It is at least more likely that she should die from a perfectly well-known and fatal disease such as eclampsia than that anybody should try to poison a woman so generally popular, though she had enemies who were both jealous of her and disliked the idea of a royal mistress becoming Queen of France. Kidney trouble is often caused by drink, and people at the Court of France—indeed, all over Europe—generally used to drink too much in those days. After all, it is only a speculation that could easily explain the sudden death of an apparently perfectly healthy woman just as the moment was approaching when she would achieve her ambition.

Henri was broken-hearted; he swore that never more could he see happiness again. Yet three months later he was paying court to a very different sort of woman from Gabrielle—to Henriette d'Entragues, a slim girl of eighteen with a bitter tongue. He was then about fifty years of age, and had led a very anxious and troubled life. He had been a hard rider, a famous cavalryman. At the end of a few weeks of "courtship" he induced Henriette to accept a document in which he promised to marry her if she could bear him a living son in the course of a year. Henriette agreed to try, and joyfully took her position as the mistress and promised wife of the King. But alas for Henriette! Six months later there came a terrible thunderstorm that caused her to miscarry, and released Henri of his bargain. But his ministers had already engaged him to Marie de' Medici; and Henri probably felt that Jove's thunderbolt had come to his assistance. By that time Marguerite had been duly divorced by an obliging Pope, who would no doubt do a great deal for the brand plucked from the burning of Protestantism. In middle age Marguerite became enormously fat, and there are many stories told about her orgies with footmen and other tall fellows. It is said that, if they died in her service, she used to carry their hearts about her in a bag, and that she used to wear a wig made from their locks of yellow hair. Indeed, imagination has exhausted itself in devising infamies for the last years of Marguerite de Valois. It is difficult to recognise this corpulent and beraddled woman in the gay young princess who danced to lute and pizzicati strings in the "Huguenots." Reine Margot indeed had a sorrowful ending, judging by the ordinary canons of human happiness. But perhaps the stories are not true. She is always considered an amazing example of the Valois faculty for combining artistic sensibility with the grossest lust. Strange things are said to have happened in history; and one must always remember her very unhappy marriage.

Soon after fifty old age, according to Sir Humphrey Rolleston, usually touches the average man lightly on the shoulder, and his friends begin indelicately to "chaff" him, saying, "Oh, you're not as good a man as you were ten years ago"; it is then that the average man, according to some philosophers, begins to feel happy for the first time in his life. Proverbs have been coined about this well-known fact, on the lines of the Greek "call no man happy till he is dead." According to another school of philosophy happiness only comes with the loss of the teeth. But sometimes the aging man boasts of his prowess as if to defy time and proverbs. Such a hero is always abnormal: either the first symptoms of some nervous disease are beginning to show themselves, or some other less subtle change is occurring in his body. His position is very much like that of a lady who, after the climacteric, observes that what she thinks to be the normal periodical discharge has returned; she does not know that this is often the first sign of cancer of the womb, and that what she thinks to be rejuvenescence is really often her death-warrant. Youth never returns; the tale of years is inexorable. It is lucky for the old man if he has some faithful friend who will guard him, and, as is said euphemistically, "keep him out of mischief"—that is to say, keep him from catching syphilis, which is a terrible thing in old age, or at any age. The old man thus afflicted seems absolutely to go mad about women; dignity, honour, decency, and all else, are forgotten.

When to ordinary senility there is added the intolerable desire that accompanies such trouble as I have mentioned, all other considerations are cast to the winds. After his marriage to Marie de' Medici Henri abandoned even the pretence of decency. Marie seems to have had to let him go his own way. As for him, he complained that she made his life a hell upon earth, and he attempted to assuage his wounded feelings with every other girl who came his way. There were many such who yielded to the king while they mocked at the elderly man with their younger lovers. Then, in 1609 he met Charlotte de Montmorency, a charming and beautiful maiden of fifteen. He saw her while she was rehearsing for a mask, dressed up as a nymph of Diana.

He was passionately arrested by her beauty, but soon afterwards was laid up with an attack of gout. Alas, Charlotte was already engaged to a M. de Bassompierre; but this did not daunt the conqueror of Gabrielle d'Estrees. He had dealt with such trifles before. As he lay groaning with the gout he thought out a brilliant scheme, which he amazingly proposed to M. de Bassompierre. He sent for the young man, told him that he was frantically in love with Charlotte, and asked him to give up the idea of marrying her so that the damsel should be free to become Henri's platonic mistress, with all her virginal beauty untouched. And de Bassompierre actually agreed to give up his bride. Naturally Charlotte was deeply aggrieved, and gave her easy-going and youthful lover such a withering glance that he retired in mortification to his own room and could not eat for three days. But that did not mean that Henri was to possess her; for, in the easy fashion of those days, he married her to the Prince de Condé, who was supposed to think only of hunting and field-sports and not at all about women. But Condé's nature changed after marriage to a beautiful girl, as any cynic might have expected; and he became mightily annoyed when he saw the king aping the young man in silks and satins, and paying violent court to his beautiful young wife; nor was Charlotte so discreet as she might have been, for she received from him desperate love-letters and poems, and answered them erotically and foolishly. The young husband and the elderly lover quarrelled fiercely, and Henri lost what dignity he still possessed. Then Condé took her away for safety to a castle near Flanders; Henri followed, and stood by the roadside, disguised as one of his own huntsmen, with a patch over one eye that he might have the joy of gazing upon her for a moment. Seeing her at a window, he would bow and kiss his hand, placing the other hand over his heart, and assuming all the ridiculous antics of an elderly lover on the stage. The Duc de Montmorency, her father, wished Charlotte to yield that he might gain the favour of the king. When Condé heard this he thought he had better take more active measures, so the young couple hastened over the border, whither Henri could not follow them. The actual details of the next few months are not very interesting; they simply represent the frantic efforts of a man who was getting senile to gratify an adulterous passion. It is said that he even threatened war with Spain for Charlotte's bright eyes, but this is probably not true. Henri loved his country enough to prevent him from doing anything so wicked. But if his prostate was not growing too large he showed all the mental symptoms of it so far as we can tell to-day. The incident is one of the most painful in history, and calls for all one's sympathy with the "sorrows of a poor old man."

Then came Ravaillac and his dagger to end Henri's misery; and probably, to those who know the inevitable end of a man suffering possibly from enlarged prostate without modern surgery, Providence was kind to Henri in sparing him years of real misery and pain. Assassination is at least a merciful death to a man who at fifty-five has nothing to look forward to but the "labour and sorrow" of the Psalmist. People often wonder what further reforms he might have effected in France; but it is the common experience that a man does not live very long after such an incident as that with Charlotte de Montmorency. We cannot even guess at the cause of this degeneration in Henri and Marguerite. Syphilis would no doubt account for it; but so far as I know there is no reason to suspect it. He had done great work for France.

Besides the merciful Edict of Nantes, which gave freedom of worship to the French Protestants for generations, he reformed her finances, organised her army, and introduced the silkworm industry which has done so much to strengthen the people of that amazing country. The French have long ago forgiven his sins against morality and decency, and taken him to their hearts as one of the greatest of Frenchmen. And now, when his wonderful personal charm has long mouldered to dust, the evil that he did is interred with his bones: only the good remains in the memory of mankind.

The best book about the troubles of old age is *The Medical Aspects of Old Age*, by Sir Humphrey Rolleston, which, though originally written for doctors, should be read by every man and woman in the land; for perhaps it would induce in them a greater sympathy for the old men. "Enlarged prostate" must be taken symbolically. The whole subject of these senile attacks of concupiscence is still under discussion, and, just as you spared me a too close inquiry into Elizabeth's physical attributes, I ask you to spare me the inquiry into those of an equally great, but far more lovable, sovereign, Henri

Quatre. The incident of Henri Quatre and Charlotte de Montmorency seems to represent what is known as a "psychosis of involution" occurring somewhat prematurely owing to Henri's hard life in the field.

Frederick the Great

IF it be true that most great men are slightly "cracked" surely this fact is proved by the peculiarities of Frederick the Great. I propose to defend the memory of this most illustrious of Prussian soldiers and minor poets from the infamous slander that he died of syphilis. Frederick had the misfortune to win his glory in fighting against three women: the Empress Maria Theresa, the Empress Elizabeth of Russia, and Madame de Pompadour; and, most unwisely, he tried to fight them, not only with guns and bayonets, but with jibes and flouts and jeers. His father, as is well known, was King Frederick William Hohenzollern of Brandenburg, who was famous for his regiment of giants. These colossal creatures averaged well over six feet high, and to find them Europe, Asia, Africa and America were ransacked at vast expense. Frederick William must have been at heart a man of scientific mind, for he experimented in breeding with these human cattle; and doubtless his experience, had it been recorded with true Prussian accuracy, would have been the forerunner of those results of the Abbé Mendel which have laid the foundation for the science of eugenics. Unhappily his cattle were less submissive than Mendel's peas or the Chillingham bulls, for, in spite of all the floggings and bribings to which Frederick William resorted, he was not always successful in securing his results. One day, when he was going from Potsdam to Berlin, he saw a fine strapping Saxon girl, a very giantess, whom he at once saw would be a fit wife to produce more gigantic toys if coupled with one of his guards; so he stopped her and entered into conversation with her.

"Art thou married, mädchen?" he asked her in his hearty Prussian way.

"No, kingly majesty," she curtsied.

"Take thou then this letter to the commandant at Potsdam," he said, "and there shall be for thee a dollar. Here it is, in thy hand, girl"; and putting a letter and a dollar in the girl's great hand, he resumed his journey to Berlin. The blue-eyed girl knew Frederick William's ways, and, running on toward Potsdam, met an ancient crone sitting by the wayside. To this old hag, therefore, she gave the king's gracious

190

letter with strict injunctions to give it to the commandant himself, and thereupon made the best of her way towards home without calling into Potsdam at all. When the commandant read the letter he found that it was an imperative order to marry the bearer to a certain private soldier, and at his peril fail not; experience had shown the commandant that his portion would be the cane or the royal boot should the king return and find Private Schmidt still unwed. The ancient crone, naturally, did not object, but Schmidt, who probably had another fräulein in his mind's eye, sobbed and made a great moan. Still, there were His Majesty's royal orders, and they must be obeyed, so the marriage duly took place. When the king returned to Potsdam, he found Schmidt still blubbering in a truly Prussian ecstasy, and the lady still rejoicing that at the end of a doubtless ill-spent life she had at length found a husband. As it was obvious that this experiment in Mendelism would be unlikely to be really successful, there was ultimately nothing to do but to divorce the couple, and the maiden returned home still a maid, while the soldier ceased his lamentations.

This was the kind of father that fate had

given to Frederick the Great; and his discipline seems, from all accounts, to have been terribly severe. At the age of about twenty his father forced him to marry a young lady, Christina-Elizabeth of Brunswick-Bevern, apparently against his will. It is said that Frederick really wanted to marry an English girl; and, according to Lord Dover, who took his account from the Princess of Bareith, the marriage was never consummated, for, hardly had the candles been put out when an alarm of fire was raised in the castle. Frederick hastily got out of bed, rushed to the help of the fire-fighters, and never returned to his bride. The reason of this very unusual action has been the subject of endless conjecture. The princess from whose memoirs Lord Dover drew his account was quite sure of it, because the queen, her mother, told her so for a fact more than a year after Frederick had run from his bride. It is suspected that Frederick had syphilis, and that he did not wish to give it to the young lady; this, of course, is possible, though it would seem to be rather unlike the usual conduct of an eighteenth-century soldier; and again, it is said that it was really she who had syphilis, because some time later she developed a trouble in her leg and was in danger of her life. Needless to say, that by itself would be no evidence whatever of syphilis. Another explanation of the desertion was that there may have been some physiological or anatomical trouble with the unwilling husband himself; many years afterwards, when he was lying dead at Sans Souci, the gallant fellows, whose unpleasant duty it was to wash his body, took advantage of the opportunity to examine his royal person, and issued a special announcement that His Late Majesty was as complete as any other man. But Frederick really loved his wife of an hour. He showed it by visiting her once a year on her birthday, and, such was the honour in which he held her, that he took off his boots for the occasion, and visited her in his stockings. He kept a special pair of black silk stockings just to visit his wife in, and, as he would never permit these to be held up with garters, they were always hanging down his shrunken shanks in great creases. Undoubtedly he must have loved her, and what is more important, undoubtedly she must have loved him, for he never washed himself, and yet she stood him.

The only portrait of the young lady that I have seen shows her to have been apparently a rather stupid and ordinary German girl; and it is said that she once boasted of having had a miscarriage to her husband. On the whole, perhaps a good deal of unnecessary sympathy has been poured out upon her, and doubtless that was part of the penalty that Frederick had to pay for having jibed at three women whom he had made his enemies even without the jibes. Catherine of Russia was certainly not a woman to insult; and Madame de Pompadour was quite able to take care of herself in a battle of tongues. As for poor Maria Theresa, she was probably too high and mighty, too utterly hurt at the saints for forsaking her in her hour of need, to condescend to answer Frederick in the bitter way that suited himself. But Marie Antoinette held, in common parlance, her end up. Like Maria Theresa, her mother, she was a Habsburg, and no doubt, like all the Habsburgs, despised these upstarts of Hohenzollerns. It was probably through her, or somebody equally pure-minded, that many of the stories of Frederick's abominable and unnatural vices first arose. Well has the daughter defended her mother in the combat of slander that has signalised Frederick the Great and his Prussia.

As it is vastly important to know his *real* habits, I draw a description of them from his latest English biographer, Mr. Norwood Young.

"In later years Frederick gave up shaving, and merely clipped at his beard with scissors. He seldom washed any part of his person, even his hands and face. In that respect he was very different from his father,[14] who used soap and water freely, and often complained of his son's dirtiness. One of his valets concluded from his master's dislike of water that he must be afflicted with a kind of hydrophobia. His height has been variously stated, the extreme ranges being 5 feet 4 inches and 5 feet 7½ inches. He was neither thin nor fat; in his youth he was rather inclined to stoutness, but he became very thin before he died. His complexion was tanned—doubtless because it was seldom washed, like a tramp's to-day; but unlike a tramp's, it was touched up with red paint. His eyes were prominent and blue-grey."

People who never wash themselves acquire a curious complexion which is distinguishable to a doctor at a glance, for it is quite different from the healthy tan of sun and air.

Hardly had he come to the throne when he attacked Maria Theresa, and marched his army

---

[14] A Freudian would say that Frederick's dirtiness simply represented an unconscious revolt against the tyranny of his father.

into Silesia without warning. The iron ramrod of the Prussians proved successful, giving Frederick's troops a far greater rapidity of fire than was possible to the wooden ramrod of the Austrians. But I am not now concerned with Frederick's glories, and if you are interested in them you will get a far more vivid account of them from Lord Macaulay than I would care to write, even if I could; a later writer has referred scoffingly to "Macaulay's lurid style." All that I set out to prove was that this great man did not die of syphilis, as wicked slanders have said of him.

Maria Theresa humbled, and Prussia for the first time on the map as a war-state, Frederick returned home to a well-deserved rest, and built himself the palace of Sans Souci, where he settled down to form a great centre of literature and arts on the lines of the French Academy.

He was hardly a German in many ways; his favourite language was French, and his great ambition was to be a poet. Although he could speak three languages he could spell none; and a writer in the *Quarterly* for 1847 gives some instances of his peculiarities in that respect.

When writing a letter he used to add, in his own handwriting, some words often of bitter jibe or of sardonic humour; and these words were generally wrongly spelt. Thus, he used to spell "winter" hiverd, "actress" actrisse, "old" vieu, and "pay" peyer. That he never learned to spell "pay" properly was doubtless because he hated to think of such a thing; throughout his life, economy was his ruling passion.

To improve his spelling, grammar, and poetical construction, he invited Voltaire to stay with him at Sans Souci, and everyone knows that the two poets did not get on well together. Macaulay took the squabble too seriously, and worked himself up into a rage over it, with much about Voltaire's "withering irony," and other early Victorian and exaggerated phrases. It has been left for Mr. Lytton Strachey, the man who told us the truth about Queen Victoria, to tell us the truth about the famous Voltaire-Frederick squabble, and he makes it possible to compress it into a phrase. They were two poets, each trying to overreach the other. Frederick, in the eyes of the world, won, because he had the greater poet arrested, thus winning by the only way he knew—by force of arms; also he dared to call Voltaire a monkey. In our war-hospital, I remember, we had a monkey as a pet, which used to live at the top of one of the entrance gate-posts.

When the descendants of Frederick the Great used to emulate him by letting loose poison gas, it was the duty of the quartermaster-serjeant to put the poor little shivering beast into a gas-helmet. At about that time Lytton Strachey's book came out, and I sometimes read it as I looked at the monkey and heard the incessant tramp of feet that, to me, is the chief remembrance of the war, apart from the disgusting nature of the wounds and the thundering noise. And as the tramping men, marching to death in interminable thousands, looked up astonished at the monkey, I used to wonder at the effrontery of the king who would compare one of the greatest intellects that ever lived in France to that of a monkey. Voltaire got his revenge, more deadly than Marie Antoinette's. In 1759, the most glorious year of Frederick's life, he published *Candide*, which, though a joyful satire on Leibnitz' philosophy that this was the best of all possible worlds, contained, if I am not much mistaken, a far more deadly description of the new style of civilised warfare introduced by the Great Frederick. Listen (I quote from Mr. Philip Littell's translation):

"No," said Dr. Pangloss, "Miss Cunegonde was ripped open by the Bulgarian soldiers, after having been violated by many; they broke her father's head for attempting to defend her; my lady, her mother, was cut in pieces; my poor pupil was served just the same as his sister; and, as for the castle, they have left not one stone upon another, not a barn, nor a sheep, nor a duck, nor a tree." For "Bulgarian" read "Prussian," and you will see the great improvements that Frederick made in war. Voltaire, like Anatole France, had an unrivalled power for saying the utmost possible in the fewest words; and yet some blockheads try to deceive themselves by saying that Anatole France is not of the school of Voltaire! I suppose they do so because they have made up their minds that Voltaire was a wicked man and an atheist, whereas Anatole France is at least now an accepted wit and therefore can say what he likes.

But two years after Voltaire died, Frederick used to pray to his God—if he had any—"Divin Voltaire, ora pro nobis!" that is to say, he acknowledged that Voltaire had triumphed. This to me seems characteristic of the man who bullied Maria Theresa.

Of course the Seven Years' War was a very wonderful feat of endurance for the Prussian people, just as was the Great War; and in it

Frederick won a reputation which was marvellous till a yet greater arose in the art of
slaughter. The history of it is repulsive, in that
it shows the triumph of unscrupulous burglary
against people who only wanted to be left in
peace. The results of our own war were better
at least on paper, though fortunately it did not
produce any man so great as Frederick.

But now I come to the purpose of this essay:
to show the real cause of this extraordinary
man's death.

On August 4th, 1784, he attended a review in
Silesia in the midst of six hours of driving rain,
during the progress of which he refused to put
on a coat and became drenched to the skin.
Arriving home he felt ill and shivery with a constant cough. During the autumn of that year
his fever left him, but was succeeded by a harsh
dry cough which never left him. His strength
diminished, and his legs began to swell; he had
constant oppression in his chest—that is to say,
his heart began to fail him—and he could not
breathe if he lay in bed, but had to spend his
days and nights in an arm-chair; that is to say,
he probably had what we now call "cardiac
asthma." . . .

As the summer of 1786 gradually returned he

began to improve, so he went from Potsdam to Sans Souci, which he never left alive. He was then under the care of the Court physicians, Selle and Cothenius, and the surgeon Frese. Unfortunately for Dr. Selle he hinted that the great man probably had dropsy, so Frederick flew into a rage, dismissed him, and wrote to Hanover, where there dwelt an eminent man of the name of Dr. Zimmermann, who arrived at Potsdam on June 26th, 1786. When Frederick saw him he asked at once, "Doctor, can you cure me?" To which Zimmermann, being evidently a courtly fellow, answered, "I can relieve you, sir." Zimmermann, it strikes one, must have known that men like Selle and Cothenius would know enough about their patient to render it dangerous for any outsider to offer an opinion carelessly. The first thing for Zimmermann to do was evidently to try to gain his patient's confidence, because never was there a more unruly man, especially where eating and drinking were concerned. The doctor found that Frederick would talk on literature and poetry as long as he would allow him, although it made him cough violently; and his first line of treatment was to get Frederick to promise to read through *The Decline and Fall of the Roman Empire*. No doubt he thought that that gigantic book would be a good way of keeping his patient quiet for a very long time. Then the conversation would shift to other sovereigns; and Zimmermann was able to give Frederick some of the truth about the health of Empress Catherine of Russia, whose surprising immorality must have been an attractive feature to a soldier. "But," said Zimmermann, "she boasts that her health costs her only eighteenpence a year!" "Wonderful!" applauded the aged emperor, "I always said she was a woman of supreme genius."

Then Zimmermann, seeing that Frederick was really ill, asked that he might be allowed to have a consultation with the dismissed Selle. This threw Frederick into a passion; his face flushed beneath the paint, and his eyes glowed with a deepened fury; his voice roared with anger; one fit of violent coughing after another came upon him, so that Zimmermann thought it wiser to desist, and return to his talk of scandal or literature. But he had already gained sufficient information to leave us a valuable report as to the king's physical condition. "His legs were swollen with dropsy, which also extended up on to the skin of the abdomen, and, though he was not feverish, his pulse was hard and violent."

That is to say, he was probably suffering from a high blood-pressure with failing heart, which was causing his dropsy.

Next day Zimmermann was able cautiously to approach the question of treatment, which indeed needed much tact, for Frederick obstinately refused to try any of the doctor's remedies, especially any suggestion that he should moderate his gigantic appetite. Zimmermann suggested taraxacum; and after a good deal of discussion the gallant soldier agreed to try it. Taraxacum, or dandelion, used sometimes to be given as a purgative that was supposed to act specially on the liver; and no doubt Zimmermann thought that if he could get the king's bowels to act freely the dropsy might be relieved.

But next day the doctor had once again to go over the whole arguments. Of the three doses of taraxacum that he had carefully measured out with his own hands for the king, only one had been consumed; and Frederick sat looking with horror-stricken eyes upon the medicine glass as though it had been a piece of artillery.

Frederick said enthusiastically, "I assure you that though my legs are swelled I am not dropsical. The only thing that is the matter with me is that I am a little asthmatical." Zimmer-

mann must have begun to suspect that to give
taraxacum to his unruly patient would be very
much like firing a pistol at the Rock of Gi-
braltar, but he persevered with a tenacity equal to
Frederick's own, and ultimately got him faithfully to promise to take his medicine. In the
morning Frederick started on his medicine cautiously little by little, and by a miracle began to
improve. Then nothing could be too good for
the Herr Doktor with his wonderful taraxacum.
It was saving the royal life. But Zimmermann
added another condition. Majesty must eat
less, and not so much of eel-pies. Then all the
glory departed out of Zimmermann. That ignorant fellow Selle, with his balderdash about
dropsy, was a better doctor after all, and Zimmermann, who really seems to have tried to act
in as decent a manner as was possible towards
his colleagues, allowed Selle to write and receive
reports concerning the patient's progress even
though he was in disgrace. Frederick was a
sworn enemy to all medicines, except a powder
of his own, consisting of rhubarb and Glauber's
salts. At any moment the taraxacum might be
thrown to the dogs, and the king's own powder
substituted behind the physician's back. (Between ourselves it was not a bad powder.)

"And," groaned Zimmermann, "no idea could be formed of the excess which His Majesty allowed himself in his diet; his cooks were obliged to season his food in a manner sufficient to destroy his stomach; those dishes which were the most difficult of digestion were his favourites, especially Prussian peas, which were certainly the hardest in the world. This was the cause of all those attacks of vomiting and violent pain in the stomach which attacked him after every meal, and of the severe colic from which he suffered every week, and nobody durst remonstrate with him about it."

Next day, when Zimmermann was sent for hastily to see the king he found him attacked with a terrible fit of coughing so violent that he spat blood. This is not uncommon in cases of very high blood-pressure, and frequently puts an unobservant physician off the scent. Still, under the purgative effect of the taraxacum, he began to get gradually better, and as he felt himself the subject of a miracle he ate more and more, until he devoured a pie of eels so hot and so highly seasoned that, to use the words of a fellow-sufferer, it seemed as if it had been baked in hell. After this he got an unusually violent attack of colic which he attributed to the taraxacum; and, to use Shakespeare's words, "Zimmermann's cake was dough." Zimmermann forecasted that Frederick would soon suffer from bleeding hæmorrhoids, "And how will Your Majesty like that, please?" Majesty did not like the prospect at all, but on July 12th, when Zimmermann left, his prophecy came to pass, which was perhaps a good thing for the gluttonous patient. Then Selle tried to get rid of some of the dropsy by making incisions in his right leg; and the ancient ingrained dirt in his skin took a hand in the game; the cut suppurated and became intolerably offensive. Even Selle began to lose heart when he made a second incision and the wound became violently inflamed and erysipelatous. But Frederick never lost heart: if he found that he had a more violent indigestion than ever after his overeating, he simply took a double dose of his own powder; and on August 4th the erysipelatous inflammation spread all over the leg and on to the abdomen; blisters arose and burst, and from them leaked a quart of fluid a day, by which treatment the dropsy slowly abated, until, after a struggle worthy of his struggles in the Seven Years' War, he gradually sank under a slow pneumonia, which is the natural end of man. But it is a cruel slander upon this mighty king to say that he died of syphilis, though occasionally syphilis is said to cause high blood-pressure. He was seventy-five years of age, and therefore there were seventy-five excellent reasons for his death. If to them you add years of gluttony and sepsis, caused by a lifetime of dirt, you get the real cause of the death of Frederick the Great. Did I not say rightly that Frederick the Great, like most other great men, was a trifle "cracked?"

The poet Campbell, in the last volume of his life of Frederick, gave a detailed account of some of the horrors of his death-bed, but, though interesting, they are too disgusting for my clean pages, and I shall not inflict them on the reader. They are chiefly concerned with the difficulty that his friends found in getting his body in a fit state of cleanliness for the grave. A lifetime of ingrained dirt! No wonder the startled washers found it necessary to get the water out of him somehow in that hot summer weather.

This is the truth that lies behind the demure paragraph of the ordinary English biographies: "Frederick died after a long illness (which he bore with exemplary fortitude), contracted, such was his sense of duty, by prolonged exposure to the rain while reviewing his troops in the province which he had rescued from the Queen of Hungary owing to his wonderful genius."

The Children's Crusade and "The Pied Piper"

WHICH of us can remember a time when he did not know "The Pied Piper of Hamelin?" Which of us can remember a time when he thought it merely funny, or could not recite the joyous thing by heart like his school-fellows? If the gliding years have stolen the detailed memory, at least they have not stolen the enormous impression that the poem made upon children; for we can still see the piper with his pin-point pupils and his light hair without tuft on cheek nor beard on chin, and his queer parti-coloured clothes: just like a Chinaman he seemed to us—like the poor mysterious "John" from whom we used to steal bananas and evoke torrents of uncouth gibberish. Perhaps he too was trying to tell us in his mildly explosive way how he had talked with the Cham of Tartary or the Nizam of Asia; perhaps he was telling us of some other mysterious potentate for whom he had contracted to bewitch vermin, though to be sure we had never observed any great love for

music in him, nor did his fingers itch to do anything more than heave his stave on to his shoulders or pick out faulty vegetables for the cook.
And how deliciously the piper had piped the rats
from that little mediæval town: "O rats! rejoice,
for the world is grown to one vast drysaltery!"
We did not quite know what a drysaltery was,
but to use Australian slang, it must contain things
positively "bosker" to eat. The rough and trip-
ping metre appealed to boyhood, and the queer
words that we did not quite understand, though
we felt that in a minute we should; such as
"nuncheon" and "justling." It seemed quite
right and proper to say that salt sprinkled on a
candle flame would burn green; and it savours
of the "knowledge of good and evil" to know
that it really burns yellow. It is good fun to
try to reread the poem with a boy's mind. But
it is impossible; you cannot fully surrender yourself to the poet's magic as a boy can, and you
catch yourself wondering how much of it is
really true; and, not content with the jolly way
in which the story is told, you wonder whether
it is "founded on fact" like so many other boys'
stories. That is the real tragedy of life, that a
time comes when you cannot be contented with
simple faith in good stories.

THE CHILDREN'S CRUSADE

Probably there is really some foundation for the legend, which was not uncommon and was told of several other towns in the Middle Ages when grown men were really more like children than little boys are to-day. That, I take it, is the only way to study the Middle Ages—to remember that the world had not yet quite grown up and men were not as gods, but in many ways like children. Otherwise how can you explain many very wonderful things that undoubtedly happened? (Not that we are particularly god-like to-day except some men in their own estimations; but at least some of us are beginning to have the germs of common sense.)

The true foundation is much more pathetic than Browning's poem, which to us boys seemed so funny, for we were not old enough to sympathise or to see the tragedy upon which it dances. That came later, when we learnt that "nuncheon" is not the funniest thing in the world and life has forced upon us a knowledge of things other than "good and evil." The Koppelberg into which the children danced is not a "mighty top"; no crowded little bones have been unearthed from it; it is just so high that a child would be hidden from sight as it danced on its way to Cologne.

Of course one naturally accuses the gipsies, for there were certainly gipsies in Europe even so early as the twelfth century, let alone the thirteenth; three centuries were to pass before they reached their climax. According to the *Encyclopædia Britannica* the legend of the Pied Piper dates from 1284, though Browning in the poem dates it *July 22nd, 1376.* I believe the reason for his error is not definitely known; but I think it is possible to guess. On either date there were plenty of gipsies about, and no doubt they would be quite prepared to pick up an odd child or two if they saw money in the abduction. But it is impossible to believe that they would dare to try any such mighty abduction as was achieved by the Pied Piper. Europe would have gone mad with rage; probably every gipsy would have had his throat cut by infuriated parents and the race would have been exterminated.

Nor is it likely that the so-called "Dancing Mania" was more than in part a solution, because that was really a spiritual reaction from the Black Death of 1348; probably people were so glad to have remained alive that they danced firstly for joy, afterwards from "mass-suggestion." It is a partial solution of our difficulty because it began in Aix-la-Chapelle in 1374; as Hecker says, "Hardly had the graves of the victims of the Black Death been covered in"; which is a somewhat excitable way of saying "a few years." The dancing neurasthenia lasted a long time, and recurred all over Europe in several epidemics. Just so, after a terrible war, do we dance to-day, though few of us, looking at our gloomy and barbaric dances, would dream that these short-frocked maidens are dancing for joy. In 1375 it had spread the thirty-six miles to Cologne, and in *1376* the few miles to Hamelin.

I do not attempt to explain the episode of the rats, beyond saying that the story is not uncommon, that there is to this day a "Ratfanger's Haus" in the ancient town of Hamelin, and that according to the original legend the piper was accused of sorcery. Any man who studied the habits of rats and learned how to catch them did so in peril of being accused of sorcery; and quite likely Browning, writing for children, made the mayor and corporation more ridiculous by saying that they had spent all their money in gluttony and could not pay the rat-catcher his fee. "A thousand guilders! Come, take fifty!" With what shuddering delight did we hear the absurd and obese old mayor brave the vengeance of the piper in those awful words. How could he ever have had the courage to do it? The real legend of Hamelin says that the piper was accused of being a sorcerer.

But it is the children who most interest us to-day. We must find a motive which could excuse an atrocious crime and hold it for righteousness. That motive we find in the Crusades; and it has been often suggested that in the "Children's Crusade" we find the real foundation of the episode.

Although we nowadays number the Crusades in a charming regularity and order, probably the people who took part in them did not realise that they were anything but episodes in a furious and weary struggle which, up to 1212 at least, had had little more result than disaster and destruction. Children saw their fathers dragged away to the East, and, lost in a gloomy fog of war and despair, mostly disappear for ever. Their mothers and their priests told them that daddy had gone to get back the tomb of Christ and save it from wicked men; and the world was sunk in misery and poverty and despair; up to 1212 at least, the war had had no further result than the capture of Acre in 1191, the elevation of Saladin to a pinnacle of romantic glory, the barbarous quarrels among Christians, and the frightful attack upon Constantinople which had led to the destruction in hideous circumstances of that once glorious city in 1204. In 1212 the grown men of Europe had become heartily sick of the weary struggle, and it occurred to the clergy that, since it seemed likely that the tomb of Christ could never be recovered by sinful men—and if you read Gibbon you will see that many of the Crusaders were exceedingly sinful, Cross and all—it was only right to try if the innocence of little boys might not be able to prevail over the powers of evil. It is not suggested that the clergy really encouraged the "Children's Crusade," though some people seem to think that they did. All the authorities that Hecker was able to consult show that the saner of the clergy were as much horrified by this result of the neurasthenia of the time as the parents.

In Germany a little boy named Nicholas, of whom we know nothing but his name, appeared in *July*, 1212, and gave out that he was sent directly from God to lead the children to the Holy Land. Vast numbers crowded to follow him in spite of everything that the parents could do to keep the little people at home. Finding that the boys were determined to go, the parents, with true German forethought, provided them with "harlots" to keep them company and entertain them on the way. Personally I believe that for this unpleasant word we should read "nurses," for the average age of the boys seems to have been rather under twelve than over. There was a considerable number of older men and women, whose morals suffered sadly. They crossed the Alps in straggling swarms dignified by the name of armies; they wore Crusaders' uniform and bore themselves as soldiers of the Cross; some little girls joined them in boys' clothes—even then they couldn't keep the girls from following the boys into mischief, just as to-day we cannot keep them from playing that most dangerous game for girls, Rugby football; the total number of the children was at least 30,000; their real starting-point was Cologne, which you reach from Hamelin, as I have said, after you cross the Koppelberg. Many of them starved in the Alps or were eaten by wolves; crowds of robbers infested them and ate their substance and seized their clothing; they reached Genoa and were mocked at by the sensible Italians, who were sadly wanting in that faith which should lead little boys to victory against black

216

men who rode about on horses and carried big swords and shouted to Allah as they fought. The armies scattered, and it is possible that stragglers reached Transylvania and formed the basis for one verse of the "Pied Piper." Some certainly settled in Genoa and became ultimately rich and prosperous, but some of them tried to return home through the wolves and mountains, only to find their friends as mocking as the Italians, for nothing fails like failure. Some reached Innocent III, the pope, and after having been made by that astute statesman to swear that they would become Crusaders when they grew up, were told to go back home again. A few sturdy little fellows reached Brindisi and found that the sea would not divide before them; they were sold as slaves to the Saracens, and thus reached the Holy Land, but in far other guise than that of conquerors. Very few of them all ever saw their mothers again.

This is what many people now believe to have been the real basis of Browning's poem, though it is quite possible that he did not know it himself but intended it to refer to one of the idle legends of sorcery that I have mentioned. If he had known it was a thing so tragic would he have treated it in so jocular a vein?

217

Even more pitiful was the tragedy of the French children in the same year when the world really seems to have gone mad. The leader was a little shepherd boy of twelve, named Stephen. Matthew Paris in ponderous language calls him a bad little boy—I suppose he had stolen some cleric's apples or done something else equally atrocious. The children in their madness called him St. Stephen; and he worked miracles. One morning in *July*, 1212, he thought he saw Christ, who not only accepted a piece of bread from Stephen's grubby hand, but gave him a letter to the king, and told him to lead an army of children to the Sepulchre. The king of France ordered Stephen not to be silly, and forbade other little girls and boys to attend his meetings, and the parents, so far as they could, put them under lock and key. Just so and with as little success might we confine behind a feeble mediæval lock to-day a little boy who wanted to go swimming. Very few little girls joined Stephen. The heart-broken parents did everything that they knew to keep their little sons at home, and some of the boys were killed in a mad crush to get a lock of Stephen's hair; in response Stephen promised that the Mediterranean would open before them and allow them

to reach the Holy Land dry-shod. The richer
parents sent guides; the poorer boys found their
own way to the sea. The unhappy mothers
could not tell us their feelings when they saw
their sons thus dragged away by suggestion; because they could not write; but one would like
to know what clerk it was whom Stephen saw
and thought to be Christ. He, apparently, was
the direct cause of Stephen's delusion; he, and
his letter.[15]

At length they reached Marseilles and found
the Mediterranean as blue as ever and as treach-
erous. Two shipowners met them while they
were wondering why the sea had not even a tide,
far less showed signs of opening for little boys.
Let us give these shipowners their glorious names;
they were William Porcus and Hugh Ferreus.
They welcomed the boys and joined in their services, behaving, to the boys' eyes, as true Christians. Stephen rejoiced in them, for all through
the south of France he had met nothing but robbers and most unchristian men. William the Pig
and Iron-hearted Hugo offered to take them to
Palestine on shipboard for sheer love of God, as it
seemed unlikely that the sea would open to give

---

[15] Probably he was some crazy fellow of the minor clergy.
The whole world seems to have gone mad at this time; it only
shows us what the Crusades really meant to Europe.

them passage as Stephen had promised. The little boys filled seven large ships and set forth joyfully and with cheerful shouts, singing hymns of victory. Two of the ships were wrecked in a storm off St. Pierre's Rock, near Sardinia, and every boy on board was drowned. They were the lucky ones, because in time the survivors reached a strange and savage land which was not Holy, but was Egypt, where black men came on board and bought them all as slaves; and not one of those little boys ever reached France again. The usual stories were set afoot that some of them had been martyred rather than turn Moslem; but all that is known for certain is that eighteen years later seven hundred of them were still alive—but no longer little boys. It does not require much knowledge of Egypt to picture the tree of knowledge of which those little boys had been forced to eat. The extraordinary thing is that neither French nor German boys seem to have known of the deeds of the others.

The only light in the gloom is that the free-thinking Emperor Frederick II afterwards laid hands upon William and Hugo and hanged them ingloriously with several other scoundrels. Probably he did this on general principles, and not on account of the little boys.

Of course the frightful episode of the Children's Crusade is merely an instance of the extraordinary suggestibility of children. You can do anything with a little boy if you work upon his imagination and subject him to "mass-suggestion."

I believe that the date in the "Pied Piper of Hamelin" is that of the dancing neurasthenia when it attacked that town; the rat episode is a distorted recollection of some rat-legend attributed to Hamelin but which may have referred to other places; the theft of the children refers to the German branch of the Children's Crusade, whose Hamelin members crossed the Koppelberg to reach Cologne.

And the leader's name was Nicholas—Old Nick?

Some Epidemics of Social Importance

THERE is some reason to believe that Hippocrates himself, our professional father, who drew up that oath by which all modern doctors measure their conduct, knew the bubonic plague when he saw it, though he never went through a plague epidemic. The first epidemic of which we have detailed knowledge is the great plague of Athens in the Peloponnesian War about which there can be very little doubt, for it was described by one of the greatest literary artists of Greece, who saw it all with his own eyes, and suffered from it. Thucydides was not a doctor, but like Cervantes he had the eye and mind of a doctor; and he could describe a disease so plainly that many other ancient and even mediæval historians have taken their descriptions of their own epidemics straight from his with never an acknowledgment. And in Thucydides' account of that plague we get the invariable conditions of all epidemics—the ungovernable terror of the people, the powerlessness of the doctors, the abandonment of all moral laws, the wild accusations of poisoning by enemies, the selfishness, cowardice, and ignorance of man in a panic, the hysterical dancing in the shadow of the tomb. From this one learn all.

I give a translation of Thucydides' description of the symptoms, by C. Foster Smith. It must be remembered that Athens was being besieged and the Athenians had brought all the farmers into Athens so that the Spartans should find no food for the Lacedæmonian armies; the device of an already beaten nation.

"The disease began in Ethiopia and then descended into Egypt and Libia. Then it suddenly fell upon the Piræus and city of Athens, so that people at first said that the Peloponnesians had put poison into the cisterns. Afterwards it reached the upper city also, and from that time the mortality became greater. I have had the disease myself and seen others sick of it. Suddenly men were seized first with an intense heat of the head and redness and inflammation of the eyes, and the parts inside the mouth became bloodshot and exhaled an unnatural and fœtid breath. In the next stage sneezing and hoarseness came on and in a short time the disorder descended to the chest attended by severe coughing and sneezing.

There was severe vomiting of every kind attended by great distress; and in most cases ineffectual retching producing violent convulsions which sometimes abated directly, sometimes not very long afterwards. The body was not very hot to the touch; it was not pale, but reddish, livid, and breaking out into small blisters and ulcers. Patients could not bear to have on them the slightest covering or linen sheets, but wanted to be quite uncovered and would have liked best to throw themselves into cold water—indeed, many who were not prevented did so. Most of them died on the seventh or ninth day from internal heat, but had still some strength left. After the crisis the disease sometimes attacked the privates and fingers and toes, so that many patients lost these, though some lost the eyes also. Immediately after recovery there was often loss of memory, so that many failed to remember either themselves or their friends. The most dreadful thing was the despondency of the victims."

I am glad to say that I personally did not serve in the Balkan campaigns, but many doctors who did tell me that Thucydides' description might, with a little imagination, be stretched to include that plague which proved so distressing to Dr.

Elsie Inglis and her gallant band. In other words, Thucydides was describing typhus fever, which has always been the enemy of besieged cities, especially in hot and dirty surroundings. Dr. Crawfurd states that we may look upon it as almost certain that the plague of Athens was typhus fever, though he discusses at considerable length the academic question whether it might not have been bubonic plague or smallpox. At least we can say for certain that the plague of Athens showed more of the symptoms of typhus fever than of any other known disease; and if Dr. Crawfurd is wrong he had made a very shrewd guess. From my own experience of typhus, which is small, I should certainly be inclined to support him. But typhus nowadays is a thing almost of the past except in times of war. That we owe simply to washing ourselves and our clothes better than of old. It is a remarkable thing in clinical experience that typhus frequently accompanies bubonic plague, because they are both diseases of primitive civilisations like India and China to-day.

Passing over the innumerable ancient attacks of pestilence upon mankind, we come to the great plague of the Antonines which was probably the

real cause of the decline and fall of the Roman
Empire, for it is extremely doubtful whether the
Empire ever recovered from it. To most of us
this plague is remarkable for the fact that Galen,
the Roman Hippocrates, ran away from it, and
has left us an account of it which seems to have
been drawn second-hand from Thucydides. In
the Roman Empire many of the physicians were
Greek slaves and had the slave mind. Though
Galen himself was not a slave, still he was a man
of his time, and it was not then thought imperative that a doctor should, in Dr. Crawfurd's
words, be "captain of his soul." [16] Dr. Crawfurd
gives many instances of honoured names whose
owners ran before the onset of plague; and it was
not till the Black Death that we find the real true
silent courage that we now expect from the medical profession as a matter of course.

The plague of the Antonines seems to have varied in different parts of the Empire and at different times of its devastating career.[17] Occasionally
it seems to have taken the appearance of smallpox, sometimes of typhus, and perhaps at times

[16] *Plague and Pestilence in Art and Literature,* by Raymond
Crawfurd.

[17] Friedlander, taking his account of it entirely from Galen,
considered it to have been "petechial typhus," or smallpox.
The sanitary condition of Rome must have been perfectly
frightful, and to read Friedlander makes one shudder.

an infusion of bubonic plague may have thrust in its frightful form. It would be much easier for after generations to guess at the truth if only poor Galen had not taken wing and fled; for he was an acute clinician. At its first onset he fled to Campania and, finding no safety there, took ship to Pergamos. Thence, after two years' absence, he returned at the urgent summons of the emperor, Marcus Aurelius Antoninus, and after a brief stay in Rome rejoined him again at Aquileia. But there was no rest for his weary soul; again pestilence pursued him. The thing would be comic if we could forget the frightful misery of mankind when the foundations of civilisation were crumbling before the assaults of micro-organisms. Man was engaged in one of his greatest battles to the death against the wild; and the rat, the body-louse, and the direct infection of smallpox were apparently leagued in an assault upon his works. It is a dramatic thing to stand before the great statue of Marcus Aurelius at the head of the Capitoline steps in Rome, near the smell of the caged wolves, and to ponder that the real enemy of that somewhat tedious emperor was, not the Quadi or the Marcomanni, but, unknown to himself, if Dr. Crawfurd is right, the ignoble body-louse and the squeaking, fighting,

greedy Mus Decumanus.[18]   And yet he sits there
so proudly upon his wonderful horse, looking
every inch an emperor yet unable to cast even a
moral maxim at his ignoble foes.

After the plague of the Antonines we come to
the great plague of Justinian and here at last we
have the evidence of an exact historian who did
not run and could state what he saw in language
that we can understand.   Gibbon says hesitantly
that Procopius was a doctor, though probably in
truth he was a lawyer.   Possibly he was too much
afraid of the naughty little Empress Theodora,
whom he was afterwards to slander, to forsake
the path of duty and run away when the world
seemed dying; but at any rate he has left us a remarkable account of the plague of 542, one of the
most terrible recorded visitations of epidemic disease; and after reading Gibbon's somewhat excitable account of it I think that few doctors will
deny that it was real old bubonic plague that has
so often made history.   Justinian suffered from it
and recovered; we do not know enough about the
exact circumstances to estimate its exact effects
upon the world; but we can be pretty certain that
the bacillus pestis did not lay waste the Byzantine

[18] Probably Mus Rattus, the black rat, at that time.   Mus
decumanus, the brown rat, does not seem to have begun to con-
quer the black rat till the eighteenth century.

Empire for nothing. Gibbon estimates the total loss of life at a hundred millions; but one doubts if the population of the Roman Empire, even in its palmiest days, was ever much larger, and surely the plague could not have swept off everybody in the known world, though we do know that, if it really breaks loose in flea-bitten surroundings, plague can do an infinity of mischief, probably more than any other known disease.

We leave the dead old world that shook at Cæsar's nod, and leap in one moment to the very beginnings of the modern world, to the Black Death of 1348; for, though the Middle Ages were still to drag their slow length along for at least a century, there can be little doubt that after the Black Death had terrified mankind all our modern problems were beginning, if only in embryo. The original source of it seems to have been China, and the epidemic proceeded with most leisurely footsteps until it took ship for Europe. Dr. Hecker [19] in 1833 wrote an exhaustive account of it from mediæval records; but since 1833 the cell-theory of Schleiden and Schwann has revolutionised medicine, and even Dr. Hecker has to be translated into modern terminology; so rapidly has medicine changed that a book written

[19] *Epidemics of the Middle Ages.*

229

ten years ago is already obsolete. Indeed, it is not too much to say that more has been discovered in medicine within the last thirty years than in the whole previous half-million years during which man has been upon the earth; one sometimes becomes terrified at the amazing growth of knowledge. Whither is it all leading us? Are we becoming as gods? Vespasian joked about himself when he was dying; let us not really grow "pumpkinified," to use Seneca's words about Claudius, when we think ourselves becoming deified.

The Black Death seems to have come to Europe from Africa by ship in 1348. The harbingers of the epidemic began in 1347 with earthquakes and floods in China and Egypt; in far-away China the earth opened and swallowed men. Frightful portents appeared in the sky (of course I am simply quoting this nonsense from Hecker and his mediævalists) and the seasons changed, summer becoming winter. At that time, according to Hecker, the sheet of ice was formed which has since prevented men from looking upon the coast of Greenland; there were unequalled rains and the floodgates of heaven were opened in a more than Noachian deluge. Vast swarms of locusts appeared and died; and the want of the crops which they had devoured thrust man, whose hold upon the earth is always so feeble, to the edge of that slight precipice which generally protects him from the Valley of Starvation. The earth opened, and into the crevasses men fell, never to be seen again; from the crevasses arose a horrid stench. Into this world, even more starved and terrified by the adventure of living than was common in the Middle Ages, the rat and the bacillus pestis made their death-dealing plunge. The epidemic which they brought seems to have been carried from the sultry delta of the Nile by ship to Greece and Italy; four fugitives—and unknown numbers of rats and fleas—fled to find safety in Marseilles, carrying their own destruction with them. Thence the plague went to Avignon, at that time the residence of the pope; and ultimately to England where it landed in the southwest counties, taking half a year to crawl to London. As acutely noted by Procopius, plague always spreads inland from the shores of the sea, and we now know that it spreads just so fast as the rat can run and no faster. In 1348 they knew nothing about rats and bacteria, but attributed everything to bad air or evil spirits; and they noted that there was a continuance of southerly winds, which of course in Greece and Italy are hot winds and may pos-

sibly have spread the plague by bringing the ships
and their contained rats. In Germany they had
some story about a dense pestiferous fog which
smelt abominably and so was obviously the cause
of the Black Death. It is difficult to say how
much truth there was in these stories of fog,
though they are too numerous and too well at-
tested to be utterly ignored; they have naturally
been seized upon by historical novelists in search
of the dramatic and anxious to show that in 1348
everything was different from things as they are
to-day. Possibly they accounted for the prepon-
derance of pneumonic plague.

John Cantacuzenos, Byzantine emperor, whose
own son died of it, left a description that entirely
fits in with our modern knowledge of plague,
buboes, black spots and all, though there is a
certain resemblance to Thucydides which makes
one rather believe that he was adding to his narrative for dramatic effect. Strangely modern is
his description of the dull stupor that affects so
many plague patients to-day. We all noticed it
in the slight epidemic that affected Sydney some
years ago. Then again John specially stated that
some patients were attacked by a violent pain in
the chest, with difficulty of breathing and a putrid
expectoration. This looks uncommonly like the

pneumonic type of plague which proved so destructive in Manchuria in 1910.

But the most interesting feature of the Black Death was its attack upon Avignon, where Guy de Chauliac was physician to the pope. It lasted eight months, with the usual concomitants of numbers of dead so huge that the living could not bury them. As trench after trench became filled, no matter how hard the living worked, the pope blessed the Rhone and had the bodies hurled into that rushing stream, doubtless to the joy of the rats. Guy himself showed the courage that one expects in a modern doctor, and has left us a perfectly recognisable description, which is commented upon by both Dr. Hecker and Dr. Crawfurd. It is in Guy himself that our interest dwells; for at last Medicine had found its soul. His colleagues, being trained in Arabian medicine, all told him that the plague was inevitably fatal, that medicine could do nothing, and that he was only courting destruction by staying to comfort those whom he knew that he could not save. Guy himself had a theory that strong purgation would cure the disease, though he knew that the only real safety was in flight. He stayed; though whether he was prevented from running by the medicines that he prescribed or by sheer courage no one can say. His own words were "As for me I did not dare absent myself, though I was in constant fear." To be feared of a thing and yet to do it—that is what makes the prettiest kind of a man; and to be afraid only of his own conscience makes a man a hero. Guy was afraid of his own conscience, not of the plague, and therefore he has become one of the heroes of medicine. No doubt he donned his quaint mediæval anti-infection costume with its beaky vizor, and went from door to door trying to bring a little hope to the gloomy death-beds of the frightened people; no doubt he had himself to clean up the mess caused by his treatment, which must have been calamitous. But he lives in the memory of his colleagues, for we are all proud to belong to the profession of that simple-minded doctor of Provence, and try to act like him though with less messy treatment. He was a brave man.

The epidemic endured at Avignon for eight months, and Guy tells us that for the first three it took the form, in our terminology, of pneumonic plague and was intensely infectious, but for the other five it seems to have been the ordinary bubonic that was so fatal in London in 1665. Guy remained in Avignon for the Black Death, and faced its return twelve years later. In the first visitation the poor suffered, but in the second the rich; but, rich or poor, Guy remained at his post with his ample store of aloes to win the love of the dying whom he could not save. We know now some results of crude aloes which are not very pleasant, and I wonder whether Master Guy de Chauliac ever noticed them, or whether his patients ever came running to him to cure them of the effects of his aloes.

To sum up, it is probable that the series of epidemics that we call the Black Death were all different varieties of the plague; bubonic, pneumonic, septicæmic, hæmorrhagic, etc. The sentimental and journalistic Nordic nations, such as the English and Germans, muttered the horrified name "Black Death," afraid to give the thing a name, just as to-day they talk about the "Red Plague" or "a certain loathsome disease" when they mean to say syphilis; but the more clearsighted and logical Mediterranean peoples knew that the thing certainly killed them, though they did not know what it was, so they simply called it La Grande Mortelaga—the Great Mortality, which it assuredly was. We prosaic moderns simply call it the plague, whose dread name even to-day makes us shudder. We do not fear it, because we know exactly how it is spread, and that, to use Osler's epigrammatic words, all that one needs to defeat an epidemic of plague is a stout heart and a long purse. During the fourteenth century men's hearts, being very ignorant, were not very stout, and their purses were atrociously short. It would hardly be too much to say that during the Middle Ages, and up till about 1700, the greatest cause of death in cities was the plague. After 1700 people slowly began to become rich, and to build better houses which would keep the rat at a distance, so that man conquered the plague without knowing how he had done it. But the conditions in the Middle Ages must have been frightful. Listen to the words of Dr. Abram in *English Life and Manners in the Later Middle Ages* about the overcrowding, which would put even Glasgow to shame. He is referring to the Miller of Trumpington in Chaucer's *Reve's Tale;* and the miller cannot have been a very poor man; he was prosperous and on edge for his dignity. But in his house there was only one bedroom, where slept he himself, his wife, his baby, his grown-up daughter, and two undergraduates from Cambridge all at once.

No wonder the rats and fleas were rampant and the plague swept over the land. And as for the personal cleanliness of these crowded peoples, there was none.[20] If I wished to use another jargon than medical I would say it was a minus quantity, but personally I prefer the medical, because that means something and is exact.

The Black Death revived that strange and mournful sect of the flagellants, the Brotherhood of the Cross. The spirit of man, which is capable of such wonders, must needs bow before that shadow of itself which it has projected into the infinite, and ask pardon of its anthropomorphic fourteenth-century God for the fancied sins which had brought these horrors upon the world. The quaint figures of the flagellants wandered, cross on breast, in doleful procession all over Europe, chanting dolorous hymns of misery that bore the seeds of rebellion against that very God whom they affected to supplicate. They would reach a church, lie down in circles, strip off their clothing and flog each other with scourges of nails. People crowded to watch the blood flow, while doubtless the rats and fleas rejoiced if rejoicing be possible to beings so lowly. In these flagellants probably lay the real seeds of the Reformation which was to come. They sometimes seized upon a church and rebelliously conducted Mass with-

[20] Of course this mainly refers to the poor. It is said that the serfs deforested Europe in order that their betters might have a weekly hot bath.

out an authorised priest, although the pope, Clement VI, who was a brave man and faced the plague like a hero, had given absolution in advance to every patient who should be taken sick. Man wanted his own priest, and sometimes when he sent in his last extremity his priest would not come, or was dead of the plague, so that when the epidemic had abated, and the world was struggling to recover itself and reap the neglected harvests, men were only too ready to believe the stories about the priests and their women which were even then paving the way for the Reformation. The Statute of Labourers, in England, was the herald of many of our modern political ideas. Those unhappy men who died, stupefied by plague, were really dying for humanity.

We cannot make an accurate guess even at the actual number of people lost during the Great Mortality. Hecker, after taking the utmost trouble, thought that at least a fourth of the people of Europe perished, but in some places far more; thus in Avignon, of which we have the most exact information, about nine-tenths. This vast mortality in Avignon was not caused by de Chauliac and his aloes, any more than it was due to Pope Clement and his blessing. Probably de Chauliac's treatment had no influence one way or the other; neither did the question of pope and anti-pope nor the great schism. But we know more about what happened at Avignon than anywhere else, because de Chauliac was a brave doctor who told the truth.

We do not forget the plague, because it takes very good care of that, and is still, though we have long purses, the nightmare of health officials who keep their silent watch over the health of mankind.

But, in dealing with epidemic diseases that have affected civilisation we must not forget malaria. Like syphilis itself, its social effects have been prodigious. Malaria was undoubtedly, with typhus and possibly smallpox, one of the real causes of the fall of the Roman Empire. The work of Sir Ronald Ross in discovering that it is spread by the anopheles mosquito, is one of the great epoch-making discoveries of history. There are few countries in the world which are free from malaria to-day. Unquestionably it is the cause of the anæmia and poor physique of the inhabitants of most tropical countries; and Australia is fortunate in having so few anopheles mosquitoes, though we have so many other varieties of the abominable little pests. That the numerous returned soldiers who were infected with malaria in Palestine have comparatively rarely spread their disease is due to the rarity of the anopheles in Australia; but doctors are always on the lookout for this particular pest and let us hope will keep it to its natural habitat in moister countries. Probably the real reason of the good physique of Australians is that the British race, for the first time in history, has had the chance of developing in a warm climate with no malaria. We are making a mistake in concentrating on the search for the discovery of the will-o'-the-wisp cause of cancer, which, though a very terrible and horrible disease, possibly associated into the very mystery of life itself, has probably less important social effects than either syphilis or malaria. I do not merely refer to the actual death-rate from these diseases, though it is probable that syphilis indirectly causes more deaths than cancer, tuberculosis or overeating. The trouble is that syphilis works in so mysterious a way; it is sly and subtle in its effects; it lies long latent and springs up again to the slaughter after the man who is its victim has long forgotten that he ever had it; and it conceals itself under innumerable guises. The great problem before the civilised world to-day is not the cure of cancer; it is the prevention of syphilis.

SOME EPIDEMICS

We know exactly how to prevent syphilis in the male. Metchnikoff and Calmette have shown us by experimental proof that is irrefragable. That their method is impossible to apply satisfactorily in the female owing to anatomical reasons is no reason whatever for so solemnly concealing its existence from young men, because, if it were generally known to the male, the females would not be affected and the contagiousness of the disease would die out in one generation. It is painful to think of the vast mortality and misery that is caused by this one disease when every decent doctor knows exactly how to prevent it. With moral education in self-restraint together with application of Metchnikoff's discoveries, which are known to every doctor, there is no reason whatever why syphilis should not be entirely abolished from the educated world. The other venereal diseases though serious are of comparatively minor importance; even gonorrhœa, which sterilises so many women and blinds so many babies, is less important because it does not affect the brain.

My own opinion is, that while moral education should certainly be attended to, every boy should have a quiet talk with his doctor before he goes to boarding-school and still better perhaps before he goes to the university. It is common experience that more lads become infected while they are young and ignorant, during the time of their university life, than at any other time.

We have apparently got over our post-war epidemic of influenza, which sensationally minded people called the Black Death without knowing what they said. But has fate altogether done with us? Has the war really left no other sequel than the influenza? Only this morning I was reading an article by Mr. Stephen Graham in the *Nineteenth Century and After*, in which he refers to the frightful post-war corruption of women in London, as shown by the mad competition among prostitutes for the favours of men. I can corroborate that article fully, for last year I went travelling over many parts of Europe, and I was impressed and horrified by exactly the same thing. A man cannot leave his hotel unaccompanied without being set upon by these women, who are evidently starving and desperate. London, Paris, and Rome are all the same; there is nothing to choose between them.

Nothing seems to be done about this frightful menace. Let us take care lest a rival to the Black Death may ruin the people of Europe. Immorality must be paid for somehow; and it does no good for politicians to wrangle over trifles such as the German restitutions when there is a very much more dreadful menace knocking at the world's doors.

During Tudor times, when the world seems to have been almost at its lowest stage of filth, there were great epidemics of typhus fever in Europe, especially in Italy; thus reviving memories of Athens and the Roman Empire, which to the eyes of modern men seem to have been an age of beauty. Typhus is beyond all other diseases the disease of filth, war, and misery; and that it spread so vigorously in the fifteenth and sixteenth centuries seems to show that things at that time were less romantic than people try to depict. Probably, if we could get at the real truth, throughout recorded history, typhus has slain more people than any other epidemic disease, possibly even more than the plague itself.

There can be little doubt as to the identity of the "Sweating Sickness" of Tudor times. It seems to have begun with the bloodshed of the Wars of the Roses, as the army of Henry VII marched in misery, slush, and triumph after the battle of Bosworth. Very soon after the king's entry into London the sweating sickness began to spread among the overcrowded houses of the capital. It ravaged high and low; at first it spread largely among young and vigorous men; in one week it took two lord mayors and six aldermen. The coronation of Henry VII was postponed by reason of the general distress, and the disease spread without interruption over the whole country. Nobody seemed to be immune; and when it attacked Oxford the professors and students fled alike in a common terror, so that the ancient university was as deserted as it was, for a more worthy reason, during our late war.

After its first appearance, sudden and savage, the English Sweat for a time abandoned its victims, and the mediæval world resigned itself to its normal accompaniments of epidemic typhus, smallpox, and plague. Soon after the return of Columbus we begin to hear of a new and terrible disease, syphilis,[21] though there has been great argument as to whether it may not have been yaws, which is a comparatively mild tropical long-continued ailment. To my mind the fact is convincing that we find no real traces of syphilis in the bones from ancient burial-places. If it had existed in the ancient world we should certainly have found such evidences.

[21] The question of the first appearance of syphilis in Europe appears to have been settled by an article in the *St. Louis Urological and Cutaneous Review* for 1924.

But the English Sweat was only biding its opportunity; for it returned mildly in 1506; and again severely in 1517; and again, in its worst epidemic, in 1528. By this time the world was beginning to think that we were eternally damned; and when in 1529, it spread to Hamburg, the good North Germans tried to signify their belief in the usual manner by confining their patients in the best replica of hell that they could imagine. Every patient, whatever his sickness, was hidden under a heap of featherbeds; the stove was driven to its full force; the windows shut and sealed with rags; and the patient's relatives heaped themselves upon him until it sometimes happened that he was actually smothered by their well-meant efforts.

Besides the sweat, influenza recurred again and again; and slew its thousands and tens of thousands. It probably so weakened Mary Tudor's heart that she died suddenly while hearing Mass.

Now what was this dreadful Sweating Sickness which so paralysed over and over again the strong arm of the Tudors? Osler describes it confidently as what we call miliary fever; a disease which now and then breaks out in little valleys of Italy and Eastern Europe; kills a few harmless people; and suddenly departs as quickly as it came.

Of course there must always be doubt as to all these mediæval epidemics. One symptom may impress one doctor as due to one special disease, another symptom may impress another as the most important. Thus, thinking of the plague of Athens, what impressed me most was the fact that Thucydides expressly mentioned the fact that the patient's fingers and genitals used sometimes to drop off when he seemed on the high road to recovery. We see just the same symptom in epidemic typhus to-day.

It is difficult exactly to understand ancient pathological terms; when an ancient observer says "peticula" or "bubo" or "macula" or uses other learned terms, we cannot be quite sure that he means to convey exactly the same idea as the words imply to ourselves. There is always room for honest difference of opinion. But after carefully reviewing the diseases of old I fancy most people will agree with Sydney Smith when he wrote:

"The good of olden times let others state.
I think it lucky I was born so late."

With all the glamour that enthusiasts and romanticists have cast upon the Middle Ages we are probably very much happier to-day.

F. W. Nietzsche

I HAD long shared the general belief that this remarkable man died of general paralysis; but a brief study of the facts as they are set forth in Frau Foster-Nietzsche's book, *The Lonely Nietzsche*, will convince any fair-minded person, as they did me, that such an hypothesis is untenable. As Nietzsche was undoubtedly one of the makers of the modern mind it will be worth while to study his health a little, for the more we study it the more remarkable he becomes.

From youth onwards he was subject to dreadful headaches, often accompanied by vomiting and intense pain in the eyes. He had temporary strokes of paralysis, and sometimes lost the power of speech. Probably the disease from which he suffered was what we now call migraine or "sick headache." This is a trouble that is almost confined to persons of active and intelligent mind, and the cause of it is quite unknown. Nietzsche, imagining that his headaches had something to do with his digestion, used to starve himself and lead the most ascetic life; but all to no purpose.

247

Starvation rather tends to make the patient worse. As a rule this sickness tends to improve as the patient grows older; but in Nietzsche's case advancing age brought no relief. Work was impossible, and he had to get leave of absence from his position as Professor of Classical Philology in the University of Basel in 1876. Later on he tried to resume work, but spent many years in wandering from one health resort to another in almost constant pain; indeed, he said that for him two hundred days out of every year were days of pain.

This migraine is a very terrible complaint which affects mostly the elect of the earth: those whose brains are far above the average. Women are more often affected by it than men; and in them it appears to become worse periodically and at the climacteric. Afterwards it generally leaves them. Clods do not suffer from migraine; the trouble appears to be one of the prices that very clever men have to pay for their brains. Sufferers from it are generally very prone to seasickness and to trainsickness, and once an attack is in full blast no treatment whatever but natural sleep seems to relieve it. The pain appears to be so terrible that the stomach is paralysed by the sheer violence of it, and such drugs as aspirin, phenace-

who was a byword for asceticism and who did not even then realise the fame and fortune that was beginning to come to him! When they examined his papers they found 900 francs among them. They took him to Jena, where he was admitted to an asylum. Unhappily his friends had no specimen of his handwriting to assist the asylum doctors, and as it was before the days of the cerebrospinal Wassermann test, it is not surprising that the poor doctors, driven to give the thing a name, hinted at general paralysis, though they seem to have eaten their words later.

The ordinary typical case of general paralysis is much as follows: An apparently perfectly sane and normal man suddenly goes out and orders a dozen motor-cars, or twenty-three cameras, or fifty arm-chairs, or a dozen sets of gymnastic apparatus or something equally silly; then he goes home to his wife very well pleased with himself and boasts how he has suddenly become the best cyclist in Europe or the most famous cricketer. No doubts for him, gladsome fellow! Probably he will also tell her that he is God. Or perhaps he will indecently assault some little girl before the very eye of some hitherto friendly policeman. Sometimes the disease will begin with purely neurasthenic and gloomy symptoms, so that even a clever doctor may be put off the scent for months or years. But when he is examined carefully it will generally be found that his hand is tremulous so that he cannot write intelligibly; his tongue trembles and perhaps wobbles in and out like a trombone; his speech is indistinct; the pupils of his eyes may be unequal or not circular. Later come the fits and increasing dementia that haunt him till his death.

The fact that Nietzsche suffered from doubts about money and showed no sign of obscenity seems to point to a totally different form of insanity. Faithful to the principle that no doctor ought to offer a diagnosis without having seen the patient, I hesitate to say definitely what was the matter with Nietzsche, especially as Dr. Oscar Levy of Hamburg is still alive and knows the Nietzsche case intimately; but I should not wonder if the poor overwrought man was suddenly seized by something akin to melancholia,[22] that last infirmity of sensitive minds. As clods do not suffer from migraine they comparatively rarely attain to the heights—or depths—of melancholia. Under the influence of nursing, rest and protection from the attacks of the

[22] Probably, like so many leaders of thought, Nietzsche was of the manic-depressive temperament, with all the apparently insane egotism of that temperament.

world, he partly recovered, but, as generally happens with melancholia in middle age, he seems to have become more emotional and partly demented before the chronic trouble that may have caused his headaches ultimately killed him. Throughout his insanity the difficulty in speaking pursued him. "I don't speak prettily," he would pathetically say; and after a tremor that may have been uræmic he passed away.

No philosopher has been more shockingly misrepresented to the British public; and now that the bitterness of the war is over it is quite time that we should make some effort to understand what he intended. The famous "superman" was not a big bullying German *picklehaube;* it seems to have represented what a man might become if freed from conventional repression: if his instincts were perfect in every way. The "will to power" was not the arrogance that caused the war; as a matter of fact, no man ever attacked German militarism so fiercely as did Nietzsche. It really represented what the modern evolutionist means by survival value in all organisms. Possibly Nietzsche made a mistake in attributing prudery to the effects of Pauline Christianity; the very essence of prudery is now thought to lie in unconscious regrets of the old for their lost sexual power. It seems to be a frustrated wish-fulfilment and is found among people who worship mumbo-jumbo, as well as among those who pretend to follow Jesus.

Nietzsche did well to point out, as Huxley pointed out years ago, that "all men are *not* born free and equal," as optimists have averred. A little healthy pessimism would be very good for the world; it would teach it to be more careful about paying its debts and would prevent it from blundering into an ignorant war such as the last one.

But nobody who has ever seen the disgusting spectacle of a man dying of general paralysis, demented, helpless, lying bestial, an obscene body that has long survived its soul, deserted by every one but his mother and his old aunts, could ever look at the portrait of the dying Nietzsche, gazing so wistfully into the setting sun, and say that Nietzsche died of general paralysis. The Italians called him Il Santo, the Saint; so far did he seem to them above all moral frailty.

It was probably owing to his incessant pain that he could never settle down to systematise his philosophy, but had to write in epigrams.

Arthur Schopenhauer

IT is difficult not to smile at this peculiar philosopher, even though he has obtained nearly as many admirers as Nietzsche himself, and it is a dangerous thing to offend a Nietzschian. But let us treat him with the seriousness that he would have insisted upon as his right.

He was born in Dantzig in 1788; he died in Frankfurt-am-Main in 1860, a philosopher to whom both Germany and England have laid claim, because his father wished him to be born in England, and took his mother there just before the expected birthday, but the good lady suddenly took fright at the English—is it possible that there can have been anybody on earth who has not liked the English?—and insisted on going back to Germany for the confinement. I have actually heard that to this very natural whim of a pregnant woman is to be attributed Arthur's detestation of women! In that idea perhaps we may see the natural thought of all Englishmen that England is the only fit country for a man to be born in. But his father had his revenge;

for he called the little son "Arthur" and the lady, being a dutiful German wife, had to submit, consoling herself by the thought that it was a German as well as an English name. But Arthur's detestation of women is probably to be attributed to a more physical cause, as we shall see.

In 1793 Dantzig was annexed by Prussia, so the Schopenhauers moved to Hamburg. Later on, when the question of Arthur's education came to be settled, they decided to send him to both France and England; and in London the future pessimist was placed at a boarding-school kept by a clergyman at Wimbledon—poor little boy. For some reason he found the life, and more particularly the religious training of the good schoolmaster, intensely irksome; and long afterwards he referred with disgust to the atmosphere of cant and hypocrisy which permeated England at that time. *Tempora mutantur nos et mutamur in illis.*

In 1805 his father was found dead in the canal at Hamburg, being suspected to have thrown himself from an upper story; and Arthur, out of respect for his father's wishes, definitely took up his duties in an office, though personally he longed to be an author. His mother, being now free from the encumbrance of a husband—at least presumably she found him an encumbrance—took to literature as a minor novelist at Weimar. When Arthur went to join her, he found that she seemed to have forgotten the memory of his father; and before very long they quarrelled. At the age of twenty-one Arthur determined to enter the university of Göttingen as a medical student; and later on took to philosophy, and gained his Ph.D. It was probably while he was at the university that he caught syphilis; and for long underwent the heroic doses of mercury at intervals that the nineteenth century thought essential for the cure of that disease. It was not till the time of Fournier and Sir Jonathan Hutchinson that it was recognised that, while mercury was essential, it was not so much the amount of mercury as the faithful years of its intermittent duration that were really necessary; and Schopenhauer duly went through the proper course of huge doses accompanied by all the wretchedness of salivation, depression, and internal pain, that used to be thought necessary for every syphilitic if he would escape the legendary tortures of that wonderful disease. He frequently complained to his friends of his treatment; but, in spite of the sufferings that it caused him, he had in reality little to complain about, for he lived to seventy years of age and escaped the graver nervous troubles that often accompany untreated syphilis. Nowadays, of course, we should put him on injections of one of the arseno-benzol compounds, accompanied probably with rubbings, pills or injections of mercury, and insist on his taking moderate exercise in the fresh air and living a sober, righteous and godly life without excitement or dissipation. While we should be chary of giving a definite prognosis we should tell him that probably he would see no more of his disease either in himself or his children if he took care of himself and faithfully continued his treatment. But Schopenhauer, while escaping the more serious nervous, bone and skin manifestation of syphilis, evidently did not escape the psychasthenic troubles, the obsessions and imperative ideas—the phobias; and syphilophobia had him in its grip till the end of his life. In this strange condition the patient becomes possessed by an undue terror of syphilis and its results; and often the fear of syphilis becomes transferred to the fear of every other infectious disease until his life becomes a burden to him as he walks perpetually in the presence of evil spirits which ache to devour him. Probably it was to these phobias that he owed his unnatural hatred of women, and his hatred of the lower side of man's nature. He knew that these "under-sized, short-legged, long-haired creatures who were not really beautiful," went about the world simply for the purpose of spreading syphilis—made a trade of it, in short; and that he, being a man of strongly sexual impulses, could not resist their embrace, though he knew it to be death. He had no wax wherewith he might shut his ears to their siren songs, while his sturdy rowers propelled his boat beside their lair; he could not leave his house without knowing that some of them would lure him with their dreadful charms; how different the miserable creatures were from the proper form of a human being, which should be, like Arthur Schopenhauer himself, a rather short, square, blue-eyed, sturdy North German. And so his miserable life went on, carrying its own torture with it, and daily his thoughts turned more and more to the utter wretchedness of life, and the stupidity of those followers of Fichte and Hegel who simply *would* not see the truth. Probably his pessimism was a direct result of his syphilophobia.

He kept a diary in accordance with his plan of absolute self-confession; and there are many thoughts on love and marriage, written during the years 1819-22 and 1825-31, which his modest

English biographer describes as being quite too frank for publication. These thoughts were written down in English; probably Schopenhauer doubted whether the Deity understood that language, just as we nowadays are quite certain that He does not understand French or Latin. But we can leave them unread, in the certain surety that they were completely coarse.

He now fell into a quarrel with Hegel, for, as he thought, purposely setting the world against the mighty Arthur Schopenhauer, of whom probably Hegel at that time had never heard in his life. He now began to indulge in that most expensive and unsatisfactory of all amusements, lawsuits.

In 1821 he found three women gossiping on the landing outside his door; so naturally he complained to his landlady, who assured him that such a thing would not happen again. Alas! a few days later there they were again, still cackling. Schopenhauer warned them to be off, and not to disturb his lordly self. Two of them, being meek and as he thought women really should be, departed, but the third was of sterner stuff and refused. She was a maiden sempstress of fifty who lived in the room higher up. Schopenhauer incontinently took her by the waist and threw her downstairs [23] with a coarse description of her character to boot; and after her flung her sewing and the tools of her trade. Heard a body ever the like? She took him to court, as no proper woman should do, and the philosopher defended his own case. An ungallant judge decided in his favour, and naturally the aggrieved lady appealed. This short-legged, long-haired female actually appealed against the decision given in favour of the Right, in favour of the great pessimist philosopher, of the Neo-Buddhist who just then wanted to get away to Italy for a holiday! And will it be believed that an unjust, nay, an inhuman, judge would not postpone the hearing of the appeal, so that once more Schopenhauer should be able to air his eloquence. In Schopenhauer's absence in the sunny south the case was decided against him, and he was sentenced to pay the long-haired, etc., creature damages. Three years later the spinster renewed her assaults upon him, having discovered that he had injured her so severely that she was unable to earn her liv-

[23] It reminds one of Beethoven and the rice pudding, and of Henry VIII and his loving subjects. But, whereas Henry, being a law-abiding, even though impetuous, sovereign, was able to satisfy his obsessions by due process of law, Schopenhauer and Beethoven had to take the matter into their own forthright hands. And yet they say that the world did not improve in those 300 years.

ing; and this time the court ordered Schopenhauer to pay her a pension of £9 a year for the rest of her life. This was really getting beyond a joke, and Schopenhauer appealed; but unsuccessfully. Therefore he was faced with the prospect of paying the damsel this pension until the Greek calends; for it is well known that women are very hard to kill, and when they are in receipt of a pension they will live for ever out of sheer spite. But unfortunately for her she died of cholera some time afterwards; and Schopenhauer, receiving notice that he was relieved of pensioning her, showed his joy by scrawling upon the paper the appropriate—and obscene—words: "Obit anus —abit onus." Thus it was proved that from woman came all man's woes; but few men have the chance to revenge themselves on the sex by an epigram. As a rule, woman gets her epigram in first, owing to her agile tongue.

The last few years of his life were spent at Frankfurt-am-Main, where his was the most perfect instance of a quiet and philosophic life of which I have any knowledge, except Spinoza's. The fires of his youth and middle age had died down, and the ashes took a long while to become stone-cold. At half-past seven every morning he rose and took a bath, taking particular care to wash his eyes very thoroughly.[24] Then, having ordered his housekeeper strictly to keep to her kitchen, he made himself coffee, and settled down to work for three or four hours; this being in his opinion the utmost that the human brain could stand at severe intellectual labour, in which he was probably right. At noon she came and timidly knocked at his door, whereupon he left his books and began to play upon his flute. At 1 p.m. he went to the Englischer Hof for dinner; and there he ate in silence with a gold coin displayed ostentatiously beside his plate. After this had gone on for some years he explained to a friend that he had kept the coin as a wager to himself that he should present it to the poor-box if anybody should start a discussion about any single subject under the sun but women, wine, and horses. After dinner, with the faithful coin still unused in his pocket, he went home, read light literature for a couple of hours, and at four o'clock went for a brisk walk into the suburbs. His only companion was a poodle-dog, and "Schopenhauer with his dog" has become a legend; the local children used to call it "young Schopen-

[24] Probably he was thinking of gonorrhœal ophthalmia, and dreading lest he catch it by the unconventional way of a bath. No doubt somebody had warned him against the dangers of the towel. He was full of quaint ideas about infection. He must have walked in a maze of ghosts due to his syphilophobia.

hauer." After two hours of walking at his utmost speed, summer or winter, he went to the reading-room, and read *The Times*. This literature predisposing him for sleep, he went home, ate a very light supper, got out his long pipe, smoked for an hour, "and so to bed."

And this went on for about ten years, until, one day he noticed that he could not walk quite so fast as usual, and that he was beginning to get breathless when he was going uphill. By this time he had become more egotistical than ever; his chief pleasure was in reading laudatory comments in the newspapers upon Herr Doktor Arthur Schopenhauer *hochwohlgeboren* and his wonderful philosophy. Gradually praise and public fame began to come to him. A steady stream of people came to see him, among them many women attracted by the thought of the great woman-hater.[25] As his heart began slowly to fail his doctor visited him every day; until one day the philosopher was laid up with a slight attack of pneumonia. Recovering from this, he tried to resume his invariable routine; but on September 20th he had another bad attack. On the morning of the 21st he rose as usual. A few min-

[25] I hate to remind the world of the ancient slander—
   A woman, a dog, and a crab-apple tree,
   The more you thrash 'em the better they be.

utes after his housekeeper had left him, his doctor called and found him lying dead on his sofa. The Goddess Luetina, assuming her least terrible appearance, had carried him to the Nirvana where no women could trouble him.

It is one thing to write a witty essay against women, just to annoy the feminists, who, poor ladies, have such quaint ideas about men and are, in physiological language so excessively ready to react to stimuli. But Schopenhauer's case was far otherwise; with him it was a matter of coarseness in his mind and sheer lust in his body. No wonder he despised the animal in man. In hating woman he was really hating himself because he could not resist them.

And it was probably well for him that he had to complain of his gigantic doses of mercury, for, with his family history of a father who committed suicide and his own worrying and neurotic mind, he was just the sort of man to get cerebral syphilis or general paralysis. I have read many attempts to explain Schopenhauer's misogyny, but I rather fancy we can detect the real reason for it in his own syphilophobia. Some critics have tried to explain it by slandering his mother and sister, on the assumption that every man can only judge woman by the women he knows; and that Joanna

Schopenhauer and Adele Schopenhauer must therefore have been of bad character. Possibly! But he was full of phobias and obsessions. And the best thing we read about him was his genuine love for Beethoven. Often he would sit and listen to a symphony, dreaming with his eyes shut; and, the last divine chords sounded, he would leave his seat rudely, lest some lesser music should blur the impression.

I have often thought of writing a history of the effect of syphilis upon the history of the world; but the difficulties appal me. We now know that syphilis is less a disease of skin and bone, than a very grim disease of the nervous system; and so secretive is it, so it loves to conceal itelf under other names, that even to-day, though every doctor is acutely on the lookout for it, it would be impossible from the mortality returns to pick out which man or woman died of syphilis and which of some apparently quite distinct affection. All that is safe to say is that the very flower of the human race, the greatest artists, poets, musicians and philosophers, have all rested under a strong suspicion of having fought against the spirochæte before it killed them. Too likely such a history as passes through my mind would degenerate into a mere *chronique scandaleuse*, and nobody would believe it.

So long as there is this horrible and disgusting prudery about syphilis, so long will it continue to lay waste the fairest part of the human race; and few doctors will disagree with Schopenhauer, the poor hopeless syphilophobe, when he said that war and syphilis are the two greatest foes to humanity.

The great effect of the philosophy of Schopenhauer has probably been indirect. When the young undergraduate of Oxford enunciated the belief that there is nothing new and nothing true, and no matter, he probably thought that he was quoting the beliefs of the great woman-hater; but it was reserved for a mind far nobler and more truly poetical to see the real inner meaning of Schopenhauer's thoughts. The great discovery of Schopenhauer was that the evil in man has quite as much to do with his character as the good. Thomas Hardy, in writing the *Woodlanders* and *Tess of the D'Urbervilles*, was really transfiguring Schopenhauer's somewhat arid philosophy until it became a beautiful truth. Hardy, in a sense, was simply a reaction from the foolish optimism of the Victorians; from the cheerful caricaturing of human nature by Charles Dickens; from the mock cynicism of Thackeray. That some people still say that his novels are grey and unduly pessimistic simply means that they have not yet grasped the full truth about human nature. And surely Hardy's "Immanent Will" was truly Schopenhaueresque.

Healthy minds have converted Schopenhauer's pessimism into the gentle pessimism of the present day, which may be rather beautiful and poetical than hideous. That Schopenhauer could be so vulgarly insulting to women was simply the index of his own diseased mind.

His opinions about women were merely an instance of the utterly degrading effect of syphilis upon the human brain and soul.

Baruch Spinoza

THIS, the most wonderful of all philosophers, the most daring, the most scientific, was born, a little Jew of Portuguese descent, in Amsterdam on November 28th, 1632, at a time when the European world was riven by the fiercest sectarian contention; when the hounds of the Spanish Inquisition were baying hell-fire and destruction to any man who should dare to differ from the dogmas of the pope as to objective truth. He grew up to be a typical Oriental—like Jesus Himself—with all the Oriental powers of mysticism.

Desirous of completing his knowledge of Latin, he took lessons from a certain doctor of medicine, one Van den Ende, who eked out his income by taking pupils. Whether the worthy Van den Ende employed his spare time by inoculating Spinoza with what Hume afterwards called his "hideous atheistical doctrines" is not apparently known; but it seems certain that Spinoza thus early came under the influence of that series of ideas which so many people have complained of as "medical materialism," whatever that may mean. Ignorant people have, from the very earliest times, complained that doctors have no religion; that we only look upon the materialist side of man; that we are blind to ethical truth and to the eternal verities of Plato. This, of course, is sheer nonsense. It is quite true that few, if any, doctors have been burned at the stake for a point of belief; but that is simply because the medical profession has always preferred, if burning were in the question, to be burned for something that could be proved objectively, such as the difference between scarlet fever and cancer, for instance, and not because of an opinion that apparently depends upon a state of mind or upon the education that any given man has received, or upon the surroundings in which he grew up.

It is said that Van den Ende had a daughter with whom Spinoza fell in love; but the critics have cast so many doubts upon the pretty romance that has been woven between them that nowadays it is not generally believed. Some rash words of Spinoza's having come to the ears of the authorities of the synagogue, they summoned him before them to explain; but, seeing that he had already parted in very truth from the conventional Hebrew worship, and not wishing to have any public scandal among the community, the Chief Rabbi offered him a pension of 1,000 florins if he would outwardly conform and appear occasionally in the synagogue; that is to say, if Spinoza would turn hypocrite. But this was not at all in accordance with Spinoza's character, so, since he refused to be coerced, it became necessary to excommunicate him from the synagogue after an unavailing attempt had been made by some footpad to assassinate him. Spinoza drew up a protest against his excommunication, but did not publish it. He dropped the name of Baruch and took the name of Benedict; in this possibly there may have been a shimmer of irony at his excommunication, for both names mean "blessed." Such irony would be in accordance with what one might expect from a pupil of Van den Ende, who in truth seems to have been an ironical man. Later, he fell into trouble with the French authorities in Paris, and was hanged for a conspirator. Van den Ende seems to have been a very un-doctor-like sort of doctor, for it is seldom indeed that any of our profession conspire with anybody; least of all for a religious or political purpose. Marat, of course, was a brilliant exception, but he came to an untimely end.

Expelled from the Hebrew Church, and with

the Inquisition waiting open-mouthed to burn him if it had the chance, Spinoza spent the rest of his short life in little towns of Holland, keeping himself alive by grinding spectacles. The tubercle bacillus was already beginning to eat away his lungs, and men howled at him as an atheist whenever he went into the street. But already he had many admirers. A man named De Fries left him a small fortune which Spinoza refused, saying that the man's brother and rightful heir had more need of it than he. The brother accepted it on the sole condition that Spinoza should take sufficient money to keep him alive. Even of this, which was offered on the assumption that Spinoza would need 500 florins, he would only accept 300 florins annually, and gave the rest to the poor.

During the five years following his excommunication Spinoza worked hard at his philosophical speculations, and at his lens-grinding, attaining a great reputation for thoroughness in his work. A little society of doctors and medical students was formed to study the Cartesian philosophy, and by sheer learning, daring of speculation, and elevation of moral character, the little Hebrew became the leader; and thus began the extraordinary admiration for the philosophy of

Spinoza which has always distinguished biological scientists.

Spinoza attained eminence in many ways before the end came. His landlady, a Madame van den Spyek, came to him in a religious difficulty. She knew that Spinoza was good and learned, though people *did* call him an atheist, and went saying what a sorry time he would have of it when the Inquisition got hold of him. Yet she heard so much about the different sects, which were struggling so fiercely all over Europe. What was she, a decent and pious woman who worshipped God after the manner of her fathers, to believe? She would ask the gentle and learned atheist; so she went diffidently to him and opened her heart to him. Thus spake Spinoza: "Your religion is a good religion, madame; you have no need to seek after another, and neither need you doubt of your eternal welfare so long as, with due pious observances, you continue to live a life of peace and charity with all."

Just so might have spoken T. H. Huxley two hundred years later; just so might have spoken Plato two thousand years earlier; so assuredly would not have spoken Bishop Tertullian, who said, two hundred years after the crucifixion of a loving and forgiving Jesus, "Credo quia impossibile," and rejoiced to think that those who differed from him in opinions were safely frizzling in hell.

Spinoza, in his strenuous devotion to scientific truth, knowing nothing about the tiny rod-shaped bacillus that was growing in his lungs, led a most unhealthy life. Sometimes for three months together his footsteps would not cross the lintel; he lived a life of asceticism worthy of Nietzsche himself, or of a monk of the Thebaid, though for a very different reason. Eating just enough to keep him alive and no more, cheerful and merry with his friends, averse from all political and religious contention, he was proud of only one thing—his self-control. People said that he used to be vastly amused by setting two spiders to fight one another. Of course this story really represents Spinoza's interest in the weird marriage rights of the Arachnidæ. These are really extraordinarily interesting, and many a thoughtful man has followed them, with the aid of an electric torch, in the dusk of the evening when the sexes conjoin. The female is considerably larger and more powerful than the male; and she sits quietly waiting with a naughty gleam in her bright eyes, at the centre of the web. He, insignificant despicable wretch, dances timidly towards her, two of his paws held out with the caution of a professional pugilist. They meet, he continuing his excessive caution. Then a moment of love, an almost imperceptible caress, and he flees literally for his life with hell at his heels. Should the dutiful wife catch him, woe worth the day for the husband. The wicked creature, having sated her sinful lust, devours him, claw, spinnerets and all. Marriage from the point of view of a spider must be an exciting business. I do not know what are the odds on the escape of the male; but doubtless Spinoza worked them out from his own observations. Personally I should fancy that the male has about an even chance. I have often watched among the mosquitoes only to find after an hour that the male could not approach at all, dare he never so wisely. But I have seen horrid orgies of cannibalism should the husband be a shade too slow. It is feminism *in excelsis;* she, great, big, hulking brute that she is, cannibalistically eats her dear little mate with his slender and spiderly grace. And likes to do it, too. Fabre thought that it was a sort of religious rite among the Arachnidæ; but let us think better of the race of spiders than that. I have no doubt whatever that it was while Spinoza was watching the spiders at their cannibalistic love-making that the amazing spectacle of the presence of so much cruelty in Nature thrust itself before his mind, and led him to speculate why he, too, a man so good and virtuous, who had never harmed a single living creature in his life, should yet be so ill and coughing and sweating and spitting and falling away to a shadow. It was then probably that he evolved his stately system of pantheism that has so impressed the scientific world. Why should the performance of a purely natural function, one which God has implanted in the spiders that they might propagate their species, be attended with such savagery? This story about Spinoza is told by Dr. Colerus, the Lutheran divine who afterwards became his biographer. Naturally Colerus misunderstood Spinoza's scientific enthusiasm, and equally naturally Spinoza, being accused of atheism, was also accused of cruelty as monstrous as that of Domitian in his most palmy days. An atheist in the seventeenth century was known to be capable of all.

There is really little more to tell about the short life of Spinoza. He was offered a post at the University of Heidelberg as professor of philosophy, but politely declined on the score of his health. Probably he did so really because he did not care to set himself in a position where a

turn of the wheel of war might put him at the
mercy of the hounds of the Inquisition, with their
burnings and tortures and *auto da fe's* and religious wars. The real call to join his spirit with
that of the Immanent God came when he was
forty-two years old in 1674. However deeply a
man may speculate upon "God, Man, and his
well-being"—to name only one of his works—
the tubercle bacillus takes no heed of motives,
and will ever be ready to attack him if he denies
himself food and fresh air. Thus it was that his
friends of The Hague went quietly to church one
afternoon, doubtless thinking nothing of the
troublesome cough from which he had suffered
for so long; and that when they returned they did
not hear his cheerful voice, for he was lying dead
at his spectacle grinding.

He had a short life; we can sum it up in a few
words: Spinoza was a good man and he died
poor. When they came to look into his effects
they found nothing but a very little money, just
enough to satisfy his creditors; the tools of his
trade and a few lenses, which were afterwards
sold as being of great intrinsic value because he
had ground them so well.

It was many years before the real worth of the
little Hebrew began to dawn upon the world;

and then it was not the doctors nor the scientific men to whom it appealed but the poets, for like all true poets he was a mystic. During the eighteenth century, until the French Revolution began to free men's minds, he was looked upon as an atheist, and even the good-natured Hume, possibly ironically, spoke of his hideous atheistical doctrine. But the poets, in the ecstasy of joy that accompanied the liberation of mankind, saw far otherwise. Goethe begun to understand him, and Novalis, the German hymn-writer, spoke famously of him as a "God-intoxicated man"; a man drunk with the intellectual love of God. Indeed, the very word "love" is too carnal a term to apply to Spinoza's philosophy. It was probably some such feeling that led people to hesitate deeply before changing the ancient terms "Faith, Hope, and Charity" into "Faith, Hope, and Love," although Spinoza in his mysticism, and our modern mystic, Professor Freud,[26] would have approved it.

After Novalis came Coleridge and Wordsworth; and thenceforward Spinoza's fame began rapidly to extend, until it has influenced the

[26] Similarly Freud's use of the term "sex" has been much misunderstood. It does not mean sensuality. In man it has been so sublimated as to come nearer to pity and love than to mere brute instinct.

278

whole of modern thought. Benjamin Jowett, in one of his biological sermons delivered in Edinburgh, the home of Calvinism, spoke of him as one of the best men who ever lived, and compared his life to that of John Bunyan, sorrowfully admitting that the tinker would probably have burnt the spectacle-grinder if they could have met.

Like Jowett, Dean Inge also has been touched by the wonder of Baruch the Jew. "Beatitudo non est præmium virtutis, sed ipsa virtus," said Spinoza. "Heaven," repeats Dean Inge, "is not the *reward* of virtue; it is virtue itself." And again speaking of Spinoza, he says, "No thoroughgoing rationalist philosophy can explain the working of a mind in love."

Accepting as proved that Spinoza's philosophy has enormously influenced the modern world, let us consider what it really is. Spinoza's pantheism does not consist, as so many amiable spiritualists seem to think, of a kindly God of mystic light, surrounded by a fluttering crowd of disembodied spirits with a general atmosphere of worship throughout the universe. It is a highly mystical and rather stern philosophy which leads to surprising results and best explains the known facts of life. God is infinite, with attributes of extension and thought; therefore He must embrace all good and all evil. As He is infinite He must be coterminous with the universe in which there can be nothing else but God. In fact, God is reality. God is the universe. Christ, in Spinoza's view, is a mystical conception Who includes all the gentleness, all the wisdom, all the loving-kindness, of the world. He is the method by which God communicated His will to man. Putting it briefly, Spinoza was a complete monist, who made no distinction whatever between spirit and matter.

The further we extend scientific inquiry the more we confirm Spinoza's views of the universe. Nebulæ have been discovered whose light takes a million years to reach the earth; so also did Spinoza account for the existence of evil in the world, that it could only exist because God allowed it, and as we cannot understand why God should allow it, the natural corollary must be that it is a part of Himself. As his fellow-Jew Heine said: "All our modern philosophers, perhaps unconsciously to themselves, see through the glasses that Baruch Spinoza ground."

Spinoza began the revolt against the orthodox conception of a fall from virtue on the part of man; and he was strongly supported by the doctrine of evolution which was the greatest contribution of the nineteenth century to thought. One would have thought that there could be no single educated man in the world to-day who does not firmly believe that man has ascended from an ape-like animal, for one has only to stroll around any decent museum to see the irrefragable proofs in the skulls and prehistoric remains of man who lived far beyond recorded time, long before man had learned to speak or to act with his fellow-man in societies. Yet to this day some obscurantists try to prohibit the teaching of natural selection; as if it mattered! In spite of them natural selection will go on triumphant, however the wilfully blind may rage. But we have passed beyond the stage of natural selection so far as man is concerned. We now live in the age of intellect, the psychozoic age. The little naked, helpless creature that had so stern a fight for existence against the mammoth and the woolly rhinoceros has developed a brain such as never was in the world before, and that brain is beginning to take a hand in nature's game. Evolution is proceeding, not by tooth and claw, not by ravening and bloodshed, but by the discoveries of such men as Luther Burbank, who has revolutionised horticulture; of Henry Ford, who has

revolutionised transport; and of our own Australian Farrar, who, by revolutionising wheat-grow-
ing, has made it possible for two blades of wheat
to grow where one grew before. In the world of
ideas evolution is proceeding by the thoughts of
such men as Darwin, Nietzsche, Schopenhauer
and thousands of young biologists. The brain
of man will work towards perfection possibly by
birth control, sterilisation of the unfit, and beyond all by the elimination of syphilis.

The process of evolution towards righteousness
was interrupted for five sad years by the World
War, which was due to a stupid misunderstanding of that very doctrine of evolution to which
Spinoza's philosophy had pointed the way. But
pantheism must be looked upon, not as a religion,
but as a scientific philosophy. As a religion it
does not satisfy the heart of man.

Eternity, according to Spinoza, is not merely
a long time: it is really a mode of thought, and
cannot be reduced to measurements of time.
That is strangely like what one hears from countless pulpits to-day, if the occupants thereof have
opened their ears to modern thought. We are
living in eternity to-day, and should act as if our
actions were to be eternal. Still speaking mystically, heaven is to be a good man; hell is to be

a bad man. There can be nothing worse even if we do know what is happening to us after death. And no better man ever lived upon the earth than the despised little Jew, Spinoza. Except for fear of being accused of perpetrating an epigram upon a most solemn subject, I might say that it is better to be God-intoxicated with Spinoza than priest-intoxicated with the various unphysiological Christian creeds. T. H. Huxley, who was accused of all sorts of nonsense, recognised that it was necessary to create an ideal Jesus for man, because, as the critics have shown, owing to the intervention of very imperfect men, we do not really know what were His real teachings; still, we must make an ideal for ourselves; and for every man his own religion must lie between himself and his God, or it is no religion. But so long as it leads to tolerance, mercy, loving-kindness, and duty, he cannot go far wrong. All these things were taught by Spinoza, and, so far as we know, by Jesus Christ.

But possibly the recent discovery of the unconscious mind may have cast a doubt even upon the stately pantheism of Spinoza. Possibly what he took to be the attributes of God are in reality purely human conceptions. Possibly animals, being so much more under the influence of the unconscious mind than men are, do not feel as we do, and there may not be so much cruelty in the world as we suppose. We know that in men the unconscious mind was the first to be evolved, and certainly it is the last to die.[27] To that extent at least may we give thanks to God, and as George Santayana says in his essay on Spinoza to all the little men who have sneered at Spinoza: "I do not believe you; God is great."

But if Spinoza was the greatest of philosophers we must also remember that he was one of the first, if not the very first, of the critics of the Bible who endeavoured to see that wonderful book through clear glasses, through spectacles that were properly ground, because he had ground them himself. He had not the advantage of modern physiology and psychology, whereby we know that a book, written by men in a state of semi-savagery, such as Moses and the other supposed authors of the Pentateuch, must reflect their semi-savage minds and the thickened cerebral arteries which must have been theirs if they were so old as tradition states. None the less he came to very much the same conclusions as have been reached by the most

---

[27] So far as we know we invariably become unconscious before we die; it seems to be exactly like falling asleep.

learned and scientific of modern commentators.
As the doctrine of evolution has cast a doubt
amounting to certainty upon the story of crea-
tion, so Spinoza, by reason of his intellectual
love of God, has cast a doubt upon the theory
of a personal God, of an all-wise and all-loving
Father. The existence of evil in the world, so
ever-present, so clamant, so insistent, by itself
disproves the existence of such a personality.
Where was the fatherly God of the deists when
the late war broke out? Perchance he slept or
was gone on a journey. Such an absentee God
is no God for modern man. By recognising
that evil, if, and so far as it exists, must be
part of God himself, Spinoza fell in absolutely
with modern thought, only he lived three hundred years too soon. But the discovery, or
hypothesis, of the unconscious mind, has had
still more startling effects upon philosophy; for
who can now say that he is not unconsciously
listening to the voice of his grandmother when
he is formulating his most earnest conclusions?
Those sanguine persons, mostly politicians who
state proudly that they are satisfied to remain
undisturbed with the beliefs that they have
learned at their mother's knee, are probably unconsciously retailing the beliefs that she in her

turn learned from her mother, and she from hers. Beliefs acquired in very early youth remain till the end of life as if they were divine; Gibbon has shown the debt that the early Church owed to women, who were doubtless the contemporary mothers and grandmothers and had the maternal mind; dear, amiable, credulous, superstitious creatures they were, though perhaps a trifle narrow-minded. Undoubtedly these women were not persons of critical and scientific mind, though to every one of their sons and grandsons they must have seemed to speak with awful "respectability," just as old ladies do to this very day. It has been very well said that whenever one feels a conviction of absolute certainty approximating to the divine, one is probably listening to the still small voice of the "herd" speaking through one's unconscious memory; and common experience is that the herd generally speaks most emphatically through the dulcet tones of that dear old lady, that real transmitter of the herd ideas of past generations, the grandmother. *She*, not Spinoza, nor Nietzsche, nor Darwin, nor Schopenhauer, has been the real maker of thought to the present day.

Let Spinoza and Nietzsche go hang as abominations unto the Lord, atheists and capable of the utmost wickedness—but *not* of sectarian wars and wholesale tortures and burnings. And as for Voltaire—one simply shudders at his ribaldry and irrepressible mockery of so-called religion which caused savage persecution in the name of the best and most merciful of men—Jesus Christ. To that extent at least *l'infame* has passed away, largely owing to Voltaire, though personally he could not have been a very nice man if all tales are true. But certain sects are still willing to apply another form of torture than thumbscrew, rack and stake to those who dare to differ in opinion from their grandmothers.

I see that I have omitted the most mystical of Spinoza's conceptions. God, besides having the attributes mentioned, has infinite substance. That was really why they turned him out of the synagogue, and would have liked to burn him if they could. The idea of giving a body to God whom St. John defined as an emotion! God is *Love!* Nowadays the identification of matter with electricity and the modern conception of the ether is the nearest that science can reach to Spinoza's dreamings, but that in no way detracts from his extraordinary insight into the universe. Even taking Spinozism in its most material aspect, we find that the more we extend the bounds of the known universe the greater it becomes, until infinity seems to become rather more than a mere mathematical conception denoted by a mathematical symbol.

What we gain from Spinoza then—and the best of men, the best of the clergy, agree—is that eternity is a state of mind; that is to say, it is a purely human conception. Perhaps if we go further and say that good and evil, instead of being attributes of the infinite God, are also purely human conceptions, we shall come still nearer to absolute truth.

But quite clearly the notion of God as an all-wise and all-loving Father is inconsistent with medical experience. The only decent thing nature has done for man is to give us our unconscious minds, without which we should be stunned and maddened by the intolerable thunder of our hearts, the rushing through our arteries, the incessant dripping of our kidneys and even more uncomely internal parts. And the way nature has treated woman is still more shocking. Any earthly father who treated his children as nature has treated woman would be considered rather as a stepfather.

Nowadays Spinoza's pantheism suggests to scientific men the mighty forces that lie locked up within the atom.[28]   So far as we know, the universe, however vast it may be, is, in the last resource, composed of atoms.   But once again, and fifty times over, I would most strenuously say that pantheism is a philosophy: it is *not* a religion.   It is too stern, too scientific, too consistent with known facts, ever to attract the countless bruised hearts, relics of the late war, longing for comfort in their grief.

Even otherwise intelligent men often ask me whether the *Religio Medici* of Sir Thomas Browne really represents the religion of modern doctors.   The nearest approach to a talk about religion I have ever heard from a doctor was once when I heard one doctor say of another that he was believed to pray for his patients; but in that I seem to scent a savour of professional jealousy.   Otherwise I might almost feel justified in saying that *Religio Medici* is generally considered by doctors to be a farrago of quackery, mysticism, credulity, and astrology, put into gorgeous and quite unnecessarily obscure language; full of sound and fury; signifying nothing.   Probably Browne was unconsciously remembering the teachings of some old

[28] Or rather perhaps the infinite forces of the universe *as grasped by the mind of man.*

lady who had impressed the truth upon him in his early infancy—probably with her slipper.

But I cannot close this essay upon the greatest of all philosophers better than by repeating the words of Ernest Renan upon him when they dedicated the great statue at The Hague in 1882: "Woe unto him who in passing should hurl an insult at this gentle and pensive head. He would be punished, as all vulgar souls are punished, by his own vulgarity, and by his incapacity to conceive what is divine. This man from his granite pedestal will point out to all men the way of blessedness which he had found; and ages hence the cultivated traveller, passing by this spot, will say in his heart, 'The truest vision man ever had of God, came perhaps, here.'"

Nor can one do better than follow Spinoza so far as earthly intelligence can lead us. Those people whose hearts the war has left bruised and broken are fortunate if they can still believe what they learned at their mother's knee. She, dear, simple, lovable soul, knew nothing about the unconscious mind, nor physiology, nor historical criticism, nor Spinoza and his majestic pantheism. All she knew was that her sons were unhappy, and she must comfort them as best she

BARUCH SPINOZA

could. Men have always been unhappy, and women have always tried to comfort them according to their sons' needs. All good men have the same religion, and they have all learned it at their mother's knee.[29]

Of all the philosophers who have tried to solve the awful mystery of the Infinite God, Baruch Spinoza probably came as near to it as He will ever allow.

But man must work out his own salvation, and it is not right to blame the infinite God if anything fails to happen as we desire. "Let us still cultivate our garden."

[29] Of course because religion and science have nothing whatever to do with each other. Religion is an emotion comparable to pity and love—that is, to sex. Science is the observation of phenomena, which religion sometimes unwisely tries to solve by transcendental explanations.

THE END